PRACTICE MASTERS

MATHEMATICS CONNECTIONS

INTEGRATED AND APPLIED

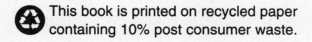
This book is printed on recycled paper
containing 10% post consumer waste.

GLENCOE
McGraw-Hill

New York, New York   Columbus, Ohio   Mission Hills, California   Peoria, Illinois

TO THE TEACHER

These Practice Masters are also available as a consumable workbook. *Practice Workbook.*
An answer key is not included in the *Practice Workbook.*

Send all inquiries to:
Glencoe/McGraw-Hill
936 Eastwind Drive
Westerville, OH 43081

ISBN: 0-02-824802-3

1 2 3 4 5 6 7 8 9 10 POH 03 02 01 00 99 98 97 96 95 94

CONTENTS

Glencoe Division, Macmillan/McGraw-Hill

CONTENTS

Glencoe Division, Macmillan/McGraw-Hill

PRACTICE WORKSHEET 1-1

Place Value

Name the place-value position for each digit in 106.3972.

1. the 0   **2.** the 9   **3.** the 3

4. the 6   **5.** the 1   **6.** the 2

Complete the word name for each number.

7. 547,000   **8.** 0.086

five hundred forty-seven _____   eighty-six _____

9. 0.159   **10.** 3.07

one hundred fifty-nine _____   three and seven _____

Write the number named by the 4 in each number.

11. 14,690   **12.** 480,000

13. 7.004   **14.** 18.345

Place the decimal point in each number to show the number named in words.

15. thirty-five hundredths   **16.** five hundred twenty thousandths

035   0520

17. two hundred nine and four tenths   **18.** forty-four and four hundredths

2094   4404

Write in standard form.

19. seventy-two thousand, three

20. three million, five hundred seven thousand, ninety

21. forty-three and seven tenths

22. eight and forty-seven thousandths

PRACTICE WORKSHEET 1-2

Exponents

Write using exponents.

1. $5 \times 5 \times 5$

2. $6 \times 6 \times 6 \times 6 \times 6$

3. $9 \times 9 \times 9 \times 9 \times 9 \times 9$

4. $7 \times 7 \times 7 \times 7 \times 7 \times 7 \times 7 \times 7$

5. $2 \times 2 \times 2 \times 2 \times 2 \times 2 \times 2$

6. $1 \times 1 \times 1 \times 1 \times 1$

7. 3 squared

8. 2 to the fourth power

9. 8 cubed

Write in standard form.

10. $200 + 30 + 9$

11. $(7 \times 1{,}000) + (3 \times 10)$

12. $(6 \times 10^3) + (5 \times 10^2) + (3 \times 10^0)$

Write in expanded form using 10^0 , 10^1, 10^2 and so on.

13. 328

14. 5,402

15. 87,001

Write as a product and then find the number named.

16. 5^3

17. 2^6

18. 1^4

19. 2^5

20. 6^3

21. 7^2

22. 11^2

23. 5^2

24. 3^2

25. 6^2

26. 10^3

27. 8^2

Solve.

28. Feisty Farlow made a deal to work for a grain company. He worked the first day for one grain of wheat. The second day he worked for two grains of wheat. The third day he worked for four grains of wheat. Each day the amount doubled. Express the number of grains of wheat that Feisty earned on the 10th day as a power.

PRACTICE WORKSHEET 1-3

Comparing Whole Numbers and Decimals

Fill in the blank with >, <, or = to make a true sentence.

1. 6 _____ 60

2. 0.80 _____ 0.8

3. 140 _____ 104

4. 0.72 _____ 0.8

5. 1.5 _____ 1.50

6. 3,200 _____ 3,020

7. 5.23 _____ 5.3

8. 8.9 _____ 8.88

9. 393 _____ 339

10. 989 _____ 998

11. 0.20 _____ 0.02

12. 1.56 _____ 1.55

13. 0.99 _____ 1.00

14. 13.4 _____ 1.43

Order the numbers from least to greatest.

15. 2,041; 2,001; 2,341; 2,011

16. 3,342; 3,234; 4,332; 3,432; 2,432

17. 0.7, 0.67, 0.51, 0.03, 0.07

18. 0.8, 1.08, 1.8, 0.08, 1.88

19. 754,004; 75,403; 754,011; 745,004

20. 2.12, 1.2, 1.112, 2.121

21. 8.91, 8.919, 8.98, 8.989, 8.198

22. 1.3, 1.03, 1.303, 1.313, 1.033

Glencoe Division, Macmillan/McGraw-Hill

PRACTICE WORKSHEET 1-4

Rounding Whole Numbers and Decimals

Round each number to the nearest whole number.

1. 8.3   2. 7.42   3. 321.68   4. 0.007

Round each number to the nearest thousand.

5. 2,703   6. 27,439   7. 882   8. 6,499

Round each number to the nearest tenth.

9. 4.71   10. 32.28   11. 178.69   12. 39.04

Round each number to the nearest hundredth.

13. 2.376   14. 0.039   15. 7.222   16. 3.4083

Round each number to the underlined place-value position.

17. 6_4_8   18. 93.1_7_4   19. 7.6_3_5   20. _5_,298

21. 57.7_99_   22. 17,_8_62   23. 0.00_81_   24. 6_0_.519

25. 0.7_35_   26. _9_72   27. 2_0_1.899   28. 0.9_999_

Round each number to the nearest hundredth, tenth, and whole number.

29. 7.893   30. 149.0769   31. 9.598   32. 0.0895

Glencoe Division, Macmillan/McGraw-Hill

Name _____   Date _____

PRACTICE WORKSHEET 1-5

Applications: Using Tax Tables

Ten people work for the Xenon Gas Station. The table below shows their taxable income, filing status, federal withholding tax, and whether additional taxes are owed or a refund is due.

Use the tax table at the right to complete the table below.

If line 37 (taxable income) is—		And you are—			
At least	But less than	Single	Married filing jointly	Married filing separately	Head of a house-hold
				Your tax is—	
10,000					
10,000	10,050	1,058	799	1,212	989
10,050	10,100	1,066	806	1,221	997
10,100	10,150	1,074	813	1,230	1,006
10,150	10,200	1,082	820	1,239	1,014
10,200	10,250	1,090	827	1,248	1,023
10,250	10,300	1,098	834	1,257	1,031
10,300	10,350	1,106	841	1,266	1,040
10,350	10,400	1,114	848	1,275	1,048
10,400	10,450	1,122	855	1,284	1,057
10,450	10,500	1,130	862	1,293	1,065
10,500	10,550	1,138	869	1,302	1,074
10,550	10,600	1,146	876	1,313	1,082
10,600	10,650	1,154	883	1,324	1,091
10,650	10,700	1,162	890	1,335	1,099
10,700	10,750	1,170	897	1,346	1,108
10,750	10,800	1,178	904	1,357	1,116

Name	Taxable Income	Filing Status	Federal Tax Withheld	Additional Tax Owed	Amount of Refund
Raul	$10,112	hh	$998	**1.**	none
Paula	$10,762	s	**2.**	$269.05	none
Anoki	$10,433	mj	$910	none	**3.**
Lewis	$10,525	**4.**	$930	$208.00	none
Shamu	$10,340	ms	**5.**	none	$44
Christin	$10,613	**6.**	$900	none	**7.**
Pamela	$10,701	hh	**8.**	$52	none
Dan	$10,155	ms	$1,424	**9.**	**10.**
Kerry	$10,205	s	**11.**	**12.**	$153
Mel	$10,111	**13.**	$999	$75	**14.**

Glencoe Division, Macmillan/McGraw-Hill

PRACTICE WORKSHEET 1-6

Estimating Sums and Differences

Estimate.

1. 482
    + 890

2. $4.37
    + 0.93

3. 34.7
    − 0.84

4. 837
    − 359

5. 438
    568
    + 1,389

6. 7.33
    40.27
    + 0.6

7. 3,823
    477
    + 5,789

8. 0.27
    16.8
    + 0.34

9. 872
    − 586

10. $86.06
    − 28.49

11. 0.63
    − 0.38

12. 72,685
    − 4,499

13. 0.89 + 2.3

14. 81 − 18

15. 7.04 − 0.8

Solve. Round.

16. There are 345 white pages and 783 yellow pages in the local telephone directory. About how many more yellow pages than white pages does the directory contain?

17. A truck weighing 6,675 pounds is carrying a load of apples weighing 953 pounds. About how much do the truck and the apples weigh?

Solve. Round to the nearest dollar.

18. Lenny bought a shirt for $17.89. About how much change will he receive from a $20 bill?

19. Judy has $30. Can she afford to buy a belt for $5.67, a skirt for $14.29, and tights for $13.95?

PRACTICE WORKSHEET 1-7

Estimating Products and Quotients.

Estimate.

1. 5.03×9.37

2. 112×694

3. 87.7×18.3

4. 0.803×483.5

5. 96×58

6. 375.5×28.1

7. $\begin{array}{r} 490 \\ \times\ \ 7 \\ \hline \end{array}$

8. $\begin{array}{r} 32.9 \\ \times\ \ 68 \\ \hline \end{array}$

9. $\begin{array}{r} 7,288 \\ \times\ 315 \\ \hline \end{array}$

10. $\begin{array}{r} 5,399 \\ \times\ 0.79 \\ \hline \end{array}$

11. $\begin{array}{r} 7,831 \\ \times\ 4.8 \\ \hline \end{array}$

12. $\begin{array}{r} 3,900 \\ \times\ 49 \\ \hline \end{array}$

13. $358 \div 91$

14. $735.4 \div 76.9$

15. $7,175 \div 9$

16. $1,680 \div 38$

17. $5,139 \div 194$

18. $2,000 \div 6.9$

19. $8\overline{)395}$

20. $7.2\overline{)50.2}$

21. $47\overline{)97}$

22. $79\overline{)55,794}$

23. $41\overline{)\$15.85}$

24. $8.5\overline{)\$25.63}$

25. $58\overline{)5,360}$

26. $29\overline{)2,000}$

27. $4.8\overline{)345.9}$

PRACTICE WORKSHEET 1-8

Problem Solving Strategy: Matrix Logic

Use the clues to complete a matrix table for each problem below.

1. George, Gene, and Gina each have a favorite vegetable. None of the vegetables is the same. The three vegetables are broccoli, carrots, and peas. Use the table and the clues below to find out who likes which vegetable.
   a. The boys like green vegetables.
   b. Gene's vegetable is not round.

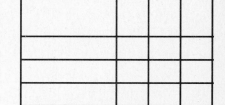

2. Michael, Mandy, Mario, and Maude all like different flavors of ice cream. Use a table to find out which person likes each flavor of ice cream best. The flavors are vanilla, chocolate, butterscotch, and strawberry.
   a. Michael does not like fruit-flavored ice cream.
   b. Mandy likes butterscotch.
   c. Mario does not like vanilla or chocolate.
   d. Maude does not like vanilla.

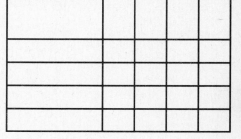

3. Cathy, Carlos, Charles, and Carrie all have favorite numbers that are different from one another. The numbers are 2, 3, 5, and 7, but are not necessarily in that order. Use a table to find out which person has which favorite number.
   a. Carrie's favorite number is less than 6 and greater than 2.
   b. Cathy likes the number that divides into 10 evenly.
   c. Carlos likes the greatest number.
   d. Charles likes the even number.

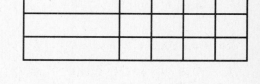

4. Four friends, Fred, Flora, Frank and Fran each have different phone area codes. The area codes they have are 201, 203, 212, and 213. Use the table to find each friend's area code.
   a. The sum of the digits in Fred's area code is not 5.
   b. No girl has an area code the sum of whose digits is divisible by 3.
   c. There is no 0 in Fred's or Fran's area code.

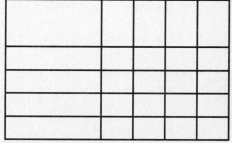

Glencoe Division, Macmillan/McGraw-Hill

PRACTICE WORKSHEET 1-9

Order of Operations

Name the operation that should be done first.

1. $7 + 6 \div 2$

2. $8 \times 3^2 \div 3$

3. $2 \times (12 - 4)$

4. $6 + 8 - 3$

5. $16 \div 4 \times 2^2$

6. $63 \div (4 + 3)$

7. $[(2 + 3) \times 7] - 4^2$

8. $52 \times [6 + (14 \div 2)]$

Find the value of each expression.

9. $63 \div (4 + 5)$

10. $12 + 7 \times 3^2$

11. $4 \times 5 - 3$

12. $24 \div 6 \times 2^2$

13. $24 \div (6 \times 2)$

14. $48 \div 6 \div 2$

15. $3^2 + 9 \times 5$

16. $7 - 3 + 9$

17. $52 \div 4 + 9$

18. $8 + 12 \div 4$

19. $21 - 6 - 4$

20. $(3^2 + 5) \times 7$

21. $(8 + 12) \div 4$

22. $21 - (6 - 4)$

23. $(3 + 5) \times 7$

24. $48 + 8 \div 4$

25. $(26 - 6) - 4^2$

26. $3 + 5 \times 7$

27. $27 \div (2 \times 4 + 1)$

28. $10^2 + (16 + 9 \times 7)$

29. $[36 \div (5 + 8 \div 2) + 1]$

30. $18 + [15 - (8 - 1)] \times 3$

31. $[(6 + 3) \times 4] \div [7 \times 2 - 2]$

32. $[2 + (3 - 1)] \times [(8 - 6)^2 \times 3]$

Write an expression and solve.

33. Jane packed 6 hams in a shipping crate. Each ham weighs 5 pounds. The crate weighs 2 pounds. How much does the total package weigh?

34. Martha wrote checks to each of her 7 grandchildren. The older three received $15 each. The others received $10. What was the total of Martha's checks?

35. Stella correctly answered 19 problems on a math test. Six of the problems were worth 5 points each. The others were worth 4 points each. What was Stella's score?

36. Manuel sold 72 daily newspapers at 35¢ each and 75 Sunday newspapers at $1.25 each. What was his total income?

Glencoe Division, Macmillan/McGraw-Hill

PRACTICE WORKSHEET 1-10

Evaluating Expressions

Find the value of each expression.

1. $16 - 4 \times 3 + 2$
2. $15 + 3^2$
3. $15 \div 3 + 4 \times 8$

4. $4 \times (9 + 3)$
5. $4 \times 2^2 - 2 \times 2$
6. $5^2 - 3(5) - 8$

Find the value of each expression if n = 3.

7. $6n$
8. $4(n + 5)$
9. $4n - 12$

10. $(6 - n)^2 + 13$
11. $\dfrac{n^2 + 6}{3}$
12. $8(16 - n)$

Find the value of each expression if t = 3, u = 2, and v = 5.

13. $5t - v$
14. $5t - u^2$
15. $t + 3u - v$

16. $(v - u)^2 + t$
17. $3tv + 8u$
18. $t(v - u)$

Find the value of each expression if a = 5, b = 3, and c = 7.

19. $a^2 + c^2$
20. $6b^2$
21. $a^2 - b$

22. $a^2 - b^2$
23. $(a + c)^2$
24. $5(a - b)$

Solve.

25. A science lab is in the shape of a rectangle. The lab is 32 feet long by 25 feet wide. Use $P = 2(l + w)$ to find the perimeter of the lab.

26. A courtyard at a high school is in the shape of a square. The length of each side, s, is 12 meters. Use $A = s^2$ to find the area of the courtyard.

27. The math club uses a phone tree to get messages out. The president calls two members, who each call two others, who each call two others, and so on. How many are called at the fourth level?

28. Write a formula to find the perimeter of your math classroom. Then find the perimeter.

PRACTICE WORKSHEET 1-11

Solving Equations Using Addition and Subtraction

Solve each equation. Check each solution.

1. $9 + s = 14$

2. $4 + t = 5$

3. $22 - r = 15$

4. $18 - a = 6$

5. $22 + 4 = b$

6. $x + 9 = 9$

7. $(6 + 2) = y$

8. $9 + r = 26$

9. $36 - 0 = a$

10. $w - 30 = 2$

11. $196 + 14 = b$

12. $24 - p = 19$

13. $20.8 + g = 21.8$

14. $w = 4.2 + 1.55$

15. $7.68 + l = 32$

16. $t + 4.5 = 9$

17. $4.019 = t - 6.11$

18. $8.06 - d = 6.543$

Write an equation. Then solve.

19. Ten increased by x is 17. What is the value of x?

20. Thirteen decreased by r is 9. What is the value of r?

21. Twelve less than t is 13. What is the value of t?

22. Five more than p is 7.3. What is the value of p?

Solve. Use an equation.

23. When a number is added to 12, the result is 27. Find the number.

24. The difference of 6 and a number is 72. Find the number.

25. When a number is subtracted from 12, the result is 9. Find the number.

26. When 15 is subtracted from a number, the result is 7.5. Find the number.

PRACTICE WORKSHEET 1-12

Solving Equations Using Multiplication and Division

Solve each equation. Check each solution.

1. $9 \times s = 54$

2. $4t = 20$

3. $\dfrac{12}{r} = 6$

4. $\dfrac{18}{a} = 6$

5. $2.5n = 10$

6. $\dfrac{x}{9} = 9$

7. $0.3p = 3$

8. $9 \times r = 27$

9. $\dfrac{36}{n} = 4$

10. $5q = 0.25$

11. $\dfrac{196}{14} = b$

12. $24 \times p = 19.2$

13. $\dfrac{20.8}{g} = 1.3$

14. $3m = 0.09$

15. $0.5 = \dfrac{p}{2}$

16. $10t = 9$

17. $0.3r = 0.9$

18. $0.1 = \dfrac{x}{7}$

19. Eleven multiplied by r is 99. What is the value of r?

20. A number divided by 4 is 10. What is the number?

21. The product of n and 0.7 is 1.4. What is the value of n?

22. Twelve divided by 2.4 is p. What is the value of p?

Write an equation. Then solve.

23. When a number is multiplied by 12, the result is 60. Find the number.

24. The product of 6 and a number is 72. Find the number.

25. When a number is divided by 12, the result is 9. Find the number.

26. When 15 is divided by a number, the result is 0.3. Find the number.

PRACTICE WORKSHEET 1-13

Problem Solving: Write an Equation

Choose the correct equation to solve each problem. Then solve.

1. On Tuesday at Casa Burrito 136 orders of chicken fajitas were sold and 154 orders of shrimp fajitas were sold. How many orders of fajitas were sold?

   a. $154 - 136 = y$

   b. $154 + 136 = y$

2. Tortillas are packed 50 to a box. How many tortillas are in 10 boxes?

   a. $50 \times 10 = z$

   b. $50 \div 10 = z$

Write an equation to solve each problem. Then solve.

3. An order of chicken fajitas costs $6.75. How much do 13 orders cost?

4. To make the day's guacamolé José needs 39 more avocados. He has 42 avocados. How many avocados does the recipe call for?

5. Mr. Serra spent $15.75 for lunch for himself and his four children. If everyone had the same lunch, how much did each lunch cost?

6. Mr. Serra gave the waiter a $20 bill for the lunches. How much should he receive in change?

7. Mr. Serra left a tip of $3.00. How much did lunch and tip cost in all?

8. If Mr. Serra takes his children out to lunch once a month and spends $15.75 plus a $3 tip each time, how much does he spend in a year?

9. A combination platter at Casa Burrito has 738 calories. If Carlos has a combination platter and wants to limit himself to 1,500 calories a day, how many more calories can he consume that day?

10. A glass of fruit juice contains 154 calories. If Carlos has a glass with his combination platter how many calories will he have had at Casa Burrito?

Glencoe Division, Macmillan/McGraw-Hill

PRACTICE WORKSHEET 2-1

Adding Whole Numbers

Add.

1. 48
   + 6

2. 24
   + 69

3. 487
   + 215

4. 396
   + 77

5. 543
   + 8

6. 936
   + 4,173

7. 8,318
   + 1,236

8. 3,807
   + 4,524

9. 7,565
   + 936

10. 48
   + 6,154

11. 1,346
   + 56,672

12. 38,416
   + 2,618

13. 73,281
   + 15,765

14. 797
   + 39,044

15. 43,167
   + 68

16. 5,783 + 1,764

17. 5,383 + 279

18. 3,088 + 25,921

19. 52,675 + 3,678

20. 493 + 38,267

21. 72,786 + 45,439

Solve. Use the chart.

22. How many immigrants came to the U.S. during 1921–1940?

23. How many immigrants came to the U.S. during 1941–1960?

24. How many immigrants came to the U.S. during 1961–1980?

Immigrants to the U.S. from all countries	
1921–1930	4,107,209
1931–1940	528,431
1941–1950	1,035,039
1951–1960	2,515,479
1961–1970	3,321,777
1971–1980	4,493,314

Glencoe Division, Macmillan/McGraw-Hill

PRACTICE WORKSHEET 2-2

Adding Decimals

Add.

1. 0.3
    + 0.6
    _____

2. 0.4
    + 0.7
    _____

3. 0.7
    + 0.2
    _____

4. 0.9
    + 0.8
    _____

5. 7.3
    + 1.8
    _____

6. 3.4
    + 2.5
    _____

7. 5.6
    + 1.2
    _____

8. 7.4
    + 4.7
    _____

9. 0.62
    + 0.4
    _____

10. 0.13
     + 0.9
     _____

11. $0.78
     + 0.43
     _____

12. $0.98
     + 0.12
     _____

13. 2.076
     + 1.34
     _____

14. 3.7
     + 1.609
     _____

15. 5.8
     + 14.312
     _____

16. 12.006
     + 4.3
     _____

17. 3.6
     4.9
     + 21.4
     _____

18. $4.78
     6.20
     + 5.16
     _____

19. 0.1
     4.08
     + 19.164
     _____

20. 9.1
     22.006
     + 40.07
     _____

21. $16.49 + $26

22. 7.439 + 0.88

23. 0.564 + 19.7

24. 0.976 + 23.4

25. $58 + 36¢

26. 6.325 + 29

Solve.

27. Nam's speed-reading times are 2.1 minutes, 2.06 minutes, 1.98 minutes, and 1.9 minutes. What is his total reading time?

28. Tina orders a hamburger for $1.59, salad for $0.89, and juice for $0.69. What is her total bill?

Glencoe Division, Macmillan/McGraw-Hill

PRACTICE WORKSHEET 2-3

Subtracting Whole Numbers

Subtract.

1. 58 − 32	**2.** 86 − 41	**3.** 600 − 407	**4.** 703 − 76	**5.** 822 − 243
6. 790 − 135	**7.** 492 − 359	**8.** 308 − 126	**9.** 853 − 247	**10.** 178 − 159
11. 326 − 89	**12.** 271 − 225	**13.** 496 − 351	**14.** 827 − 604	**15.** 965 − 745

16. 3,451 − 1,524	**17.** 1,460 − 188	**18.** 7,285 − 3,175
19. 24,002 − 16,126	**20.** 5,100 − 3,405	**21.** 47,316 − 27,213

22. 5,208 − 105

23. 3,642 − 2,234

24. 4,622 − 3,784

Solve.

25. Maureen needs $600 for the down payment on a computer. She has saved $336 already. How much does she still need to save for the down payment?

26. Yuri took a $20 bill with him to the ball game. He paid $7.50 at the gate for his ticket. He bought snacks for $5.65 and a program for $2.25. How much did he have left?

Glencoe Division, Macmillan/McGraw-Hill

PRACTICE WORKSHEET 2-4

Subtracting Decimals

Subtract.

1. 8.4
    − 3.3

2. 7.3
    − 5.4

3. 8
    − 3.1

4. 0.6
    − 0.21

5. 0.41
    − 0.17

6. $0.86
    − 0.17

7. $10.85
    − 2.17

8. 0.13
    − 0.07

9. 0.7
    − 0.36

10. 0.727
    − 0.451

11. 1.61
    − 0.9

12. $10.02
    − 0.88

13. 0.43
    − 0.39

14. 6.03
    − 0.13

15. $6.70
    − 1.42

16. $5.00
    − 2.76

17. 0.310
    − 0.042

18. $75.86
    − 1.09

19. 63,508.76
    − 51,429.08

20. 2.0003
    − 0.08

21. 11.680 − 4.23

22. 8.42 − 5.526

23. Subtract $22.48 from $56.35.

24. Find the difference of 296.03 and 84.007.

Solve.

25. The class collects $19.32 for a holiday project. They need $23.50. How much more must they collect?

26. Connie has 20 milliliters of sulfuric acid. Her experiment calls for 1.6 milliliters. How many milliliters will Connie have left?

PRACTICE WORKSHEET 2-5

Applications: Checking Accounts

*Complete the balance column to find the amount of money
Jennifer Chase has left in her checking account on April 30.*

	NUMBER	DATE	DESCRIPTION OF TRANSACTION	PAYMENT/DEBIT (−)	DEPOSIT/CREDIT (+)	BALANCE
						$1231 07
1.	201	4/1	Groden's Grocery	103.82		
2.	201	4/4	Big Al's Autos	111.26		
3.	203	4/7	Mickey's Cuisine	72.25		
4.	204	4/8	Wasco Telephone Company	201.44		
5.		4/9	deposit	—	473.53	
6.	205	4/10	A & T Insurance	386.89		
7.	206	4/11	Wasco Gas	75.53		
8.	207	4/11	Electric Company	195.40		
9.	208	4/12	Mortgage	521.57		
10.		4/12	deposit	—	713.98	
11.	209	4/19	Loan	92.75		
12.	210	4/21	Darlene's Department Store	118.65		
13.	211	4/21	Super Sundry	5.00		
14.		4/21	deposit	—	428.60	
15.	212	4/23	Hirt's Furniture	219.74		
16.	213	4/23	City of Charlesville	123.90		
17.	214	4/24	Shoe Outlet	78.65		
18.		4/24	deposit	—	628.35	
19.	215	4/25	Frank's Finer Foods	77.78		
20.	216	4/25	Pamela Beauty Salon	35.40		
21.	217	4/28	Buck's Garage	187.65		
22.	218	4/28	Galordi Airlines	213.14		
23.	219	4/30	Kelley's Kennel	97.80		

Glencoe Division, Macmillan/McGraw-Hill

PRACTICE WORKSHEET 2-6

Arithmetic Sequences

Write the next three numbers in each sequence.

1. 18, 20, 22, ____ , ____ , ____

2. 54, 48, 42, ____ , ____ , ____

3. 0.4, 2.4, 4.4, ____ , ____ , ____

4. 45, 57, 69, ____ , ____ , ____

5. 25.3, 22, 18.7, ____ , ____ , ____

6. 8.9, 8.5, 8.1, ____ , ____ , ____

7. 5, 11, 17, 23, ____ , ____ , ____

8. 11, 15, 19, 23, ____ , ____ , ____

9. 6, 9, 12, 15, ____ , ____ , ____

10. 2.1, 2.3, 2.5, 2.7, ____ , ____ , ____

11. 3.6, 3.1, 2.6, 2.1, ____ , ____ , ____

12. 8, 27, 46, 65, ____ , ____ , ____

13. 50, 42, 34, 26, ____ , ____ , ____

14. 20.6, 21.7, 22.8, 23.9, ____ , ____ , ____

15. 3.5, 70, 10.5, 14, ____ , ____ , ____

16. 65, 56, 47, 38, ____ , ____ , ____

State whether each sequence is arithmetic. If it is, write the next three terms. If is is not, write no.

17. 3, 9, 27, 81,...

18. 4, 34, 64, 94,...

19. 21.3, 24.3, 30.3, 33.3,...

20. 4.5, 9, 13.5, 18,...

Copy and complete each arithmetic sequence.

21. 12, 20, ____ , 36, ____ , ____

22. 20.5, ____ , 25.5, 28, ____ , ____

PRACTICE WORKSHEET 2-7

Problem-Solving Strategy:
Choosing the Method of Computation

Solve each problem. State the method of computation used.

1. Lisa is ordering sporting goods equipment from a catalog. She orders gym shoes for $68.95, two wrist bands for $3.95 each, a volley-ball for $18.49, and a jersey for $25.95. What is the total amount of Lisa's order?

2. Warren is planning a trip to Funworld with his friends. Warren knows that the entrance fee is $5 and that he will go on about 10 rides. The rides cost between $2 and $3 each. He will buy lunch, some snacks, and maybe a souvenir, too. How much money should Warren take to Funworld?

3. Two classes at Lincoln School are raising money for new science equipment for the school. Twenty-five students in one class collected, on the average, $20 each. Twenty students in another class collected an average of $25 each. How much money was raised by the two classes?

4. On his last bank statement, Mark's checking account showed a balance of $324.88. Since then, he has made withdrawals of $30, $50, and $30, and deposits of $134.62 and $208.03. What is the current balance in Mark's account?

5. If Becky saves $400, she can buy a mountain bike. She has already saved $252. She figures that if she saves $37.50 a week from her baby-sitting job for the next 5 weeks, she will have enough money. Is Becky right? Explain.

6. John wants a motorcycle that costs $2,195. He has saved $468.42 thus far. If he can save $47 a week, how many weeks will it take him to save the money he needs?

7. Use each of the digits 2, 3, 4, and 5 only once. Find two 2-digit numbers that will give the least possible answer when multiplied.

8. A bicycle shop contains 48 bicycles and tricycles. If there is a total of 108 wheels, how many bicycles and how tricycles are in the store?

PRACTICE WORKSHEET 2-8

Perimeter

Find the perimeter of each figure.

1. 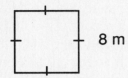 8 m

2. 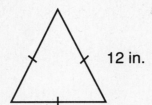 12 in.

3. 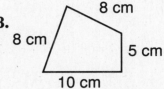 8 cm 8 cm 5 cm 10 cm

4. 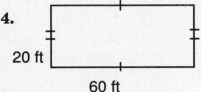 20 ft 60 ft

5. 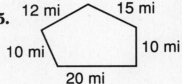 12 mi 15 mi 10 mi 10 mi 20 mi

6. 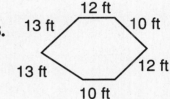 12 ft 13 ft 10 ft 13 ft 12 ft 10 ft

7. 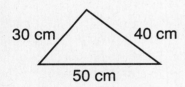 30 cm 40 cm 50 cm

8. 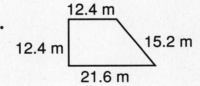 12.4 m 12.4 m 15.2 m 21.6 m

9. 81 ft

10. 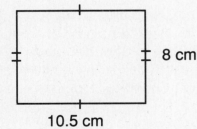 8 cm 10.5 cm

11. 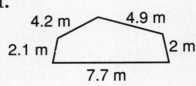 4.2 m 4.9 m 2.1 m 2 m 7.7 m

12. 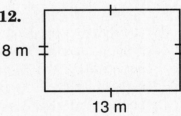 8 m 13 m

Solve.

13. The Parker family's backyard is rectangular, measuring 45 feet by 60 feet. What is the perimeter?

14. George has 100 feet of fencing. If he fences a square garden, how long is each side?

PRACTICE WORKSHEET 2-9

Problem Solving: Identifying the Necessary Facts

If the problem has the necessary facts, solve. State any missing or extra facts.

1. Marcia earns $8.10 per hour. Each paycheck she puts $25 toward the purchase of U.S. Savings Bonds and $20 into her savings account. If Marcia gets paid every two weeks, how much will she save in a year?

2. Brad has a checking account balance of $832.76. He just wrote check #235 to his landlord for $290 to pay the rent for March and check #236 to the electric company for $32.15. What is Brad's new checking account balance?

3. Charlie had the following payroll deductions last week: State Tax $52.18, Federal Tax $75.13, Health Insurance $5.76, Union Dues $8.50, FICA Tax $32.43, and City Tax $9.12. What were Charlie's total deductions for taxes?

4. The Lopez family has a monthly income of $2,450. Each month they pay $490 for rent, $550 for food, $42 for electricity, $90 for entertainment, and $70 for transportation. The remaining money goes to savings and travel. How much do they spend on travel?

5. Ralph's paycheck was $276.82 after $137.28 in deductions. He deposited the check in his checking account. He also withdrew $25 in cash and wrote a $43.87 check for groceries. How much money was left in Ralph's account?

6. Sherrie's bank statement shows a balance of $628.97 in her checking account. She wrote 15 checks, but 3 checks totaling $153 are not included on this statement. What is Sherrie's correct checking account balance?

7. The Foster family pays $520 rent each month. They average $130 per month for utilities (gas, electric, water, and telephone). They have lived in this house for 3 years. At this rate, how much rent do they pay in a year?

8. Gail and George budget their monthly household income as follows: $650 for housing, $700 for food, 10% for savings, $50 for transportation, and the rest for miscellaneous expenses. How much money do they save in a month?

9. Carmen puts hair care, cleaning, and new clothes in her monthly budget for clothing. Her total monthly budget is $850, of which $120 goes for clothing. Permanents cost $26 and she bought a $50 dress last week. What is Carmen's monthly budget for clothing?

10. Pam is paid weekly at the bank where she works. She gets a gross income of $21,580 per year and has weekly deductions of $135.27. What are Pam's total deductions for a year?

Name _____ Date _____

PRACTICE WORKSHEET 3-1

Multiplying Whole Numbers

Multiply.

1. 49
   × 8

2. $64
   × 7

3. 97
   × 6

4. 108
   × 5

5. $231
   × 9

6. $735
   × 6

7. 2,431
   × 5

8. 50
   × 12

9. $87
   × 23

10. 92
    × 37

11. 465
    × 30

12. $721
    × 20

13. $409
    × 31

14. 657
    × 26

15. 582
    × 34

16. 6,432
    × 30

17. $2,759
    × 50

18. 3,506
    × 24

19. $5,720
    × 32

20. $9,874
    × 46

21. 732
    × 400

22. $694
    × 500

23. 503
    × 307

24. $620
    × 805

25. 756
    × 327

26. 506 × 481

27. 2,407 × 303

28. $6,409 × 342

Solve.

29. If a car travels at a constant speed of 55 miles per hour, how far will it travel in 6 hours?

30. Juan is reading a book that has 16 chapters. Each chapter has 23 pages. How many pages are in the book?

Glencoe Division, Macmillan/McGraw-Hill

PRACTICE WORKSHEET 3-2

Multiplying Decimals

Multiply.

1. 0.7
   × 3

2. 2.1
   × 9

3. 7.87
   × 6

4. 0.46
   × 7

5. 0.3
   × 0.4

6. 0.8
   × 0.4

7. 24
   × 0.3

8. 0.71
   × 0.2

9. 0.5
   × 0.7

10. 0.9
    × 0.6

11. 0.74
    × 0.3

12. 0.36
    × 0.8

13. 1.44
    × 0.6

14. 5.27
    × 0.7

15. 2.86
    × 0.04

16. 0.329
    × 0.35

17. 5.06
    × 1.2

18. 71.4
    × 2.9

19. 7.64
    × 0.29

20. 5.28
    × 0.52

21. 7.24
    × 5.9

22. 0.114
    × 0.89

23. 6.75
    × 9.7

24. 0.837
    × 0.56

Solve.

25. Marie travels 5.6 miles per hour on her bike. If she rides for 1.25 hours, how far does she ride?

26. Almonds are $1.78 per pound. How much change does Boris receive if he pays for 1.5 pounds with a $5 bill?

PRACTICE WORKSHEET 3-3

Applications: Buying on Credit

Complete the table.

Cash Price	Down Payment	Monthly Payment	Number of Months	Total Cost	Finance Charge
$366	$10	$35	12	1. _____	2. _____
$900	$100	$75	12	3. _____	4. _____
$1,800	$250	$50	36	5. _____	6. _____
$6,500	$1,250	$164	36	7. _____	8. _____
$2,995	$875	$115	24	9. _____	10. _____
$8,229	$1,500	$226	36	11. _____	12. _____
$4,789	$750	$218	24	13. _____	14. _____

Solve.

15. With a down payment of $1,000, Kim can buy a $12,000 car by making 36 monthly payments of $336. What is her total cost? What is the finance charge?

16. With a down payment of $50, Carlos can buy a $489 camera by making 12 monthly payments of $41. What is the total cost of the camera? What is the finance charge?

17. A stereo system costs $1,450. Jake can buy it on credit by putting $300 down and making 24 monthly payments of $64. What is the finance charge?

18. Ramona bought furniture on credit by paying $375 and agreeing to pay the rest in monthly payments of $140 for two years. After 8 payments, she wants to pay the remaining cost. What is the remaining cost?

19. Refer to Problem 18. If the furniture store gives Ramona $250 off the total price for paying early, what is the total amount she will pay for the furniture?

20. A $4,000 motorcycle is on sale for $600 less. Anna can buy the bike with a down payment of $500 and monthly payments of $148 for two years. How much will she pay for the motorcycle? What is the finance charge?

PRACTICE WORKSHEET 3-4

Dividing Whole Numbers

Divide. Check with multiplication.

1. $9\overline{)927}$ 2. $8\overline{)648}$ 3. $6\overline{)624}$ 4. $3\overline{)930}$

5. $7\overline{)494}$ 6. $2\overline{)626}$ 7. $4\overline{)972}$ 8. $9\overline{)592}$

9. $20\overline{)400}$ 10. $32\overline{)440}$ 11. $14\overline{)68}$ 12. $31\overline{)63}$

13. $42\overline{)135}$ 14. $40\overline{)98}$ 15. $28\overline{)776}$ 16. $62\overline{)354}$

17. $67\overline{)8,143}$ 18. $36\overline{)7,288}$ 19. $41\overline{)3,895}$ 20. $52\overline{)3,652}$

Solve.

21. If Jenny drives an average of 45 miles an hour, how long does it take her to drive 585 miles?

22. In 13 days, 2,834 people visit the exhibit. On the average, how many people visit each day?

PRACTICE WORKSHEET 3-5

Multiplying and Dividing by Powers of 10

Multiply.

1. 14×10

2. 27×100

3. $58 \times 1{,}000$

4. 256×10^1

5. 361×10^2

6. $495 \times 1{,}000$

7. 7.6×10

8. 5.2×100

9. 8.9×10^3

10. 4.21×10

11. 3.73×100

12. $6.85 \times 1{,}000$

Divide.

13. $8{,}024 \div 10$

14. $6{,}371 \div 10^2$

15. $5{,}406 \div 1{,}000$

16. $436 \div 10^1$

17. $218 \div 100$

18. $153 \div 1{,}000$

19. $1.5 \div 10$

20. $3.8 \div 100$

21. $7.1 \div 10^3$

22. $0.25 \div 10$

23. $0.93 \div 100$

24. $0.84 \div 1{,}000$

Replace each variable with a power of 10 to make a true sentence.

25. $57 \div y = 0.057$

26. $3.522 \times p = 352.2$

27. $93 \div x = 9.3$

28. $64.027 \times q = 640.27$

29. $0.083 \div w = 0.000083$

30. $502.3 \times s = 5{,}023$

31. $99.94 \times z = 99{,}940$

32. $0.049 \times t = 4.9$

33. $2 \times r = 200$

34. $7.324 \div y = 0.07324$

Glencoe Division, Macmillan/McGraw-Hill

PRACTICE WORKSHEET 3-6

Problem Solving Strategy: Look for a Pattern

Solve.

1. Ralph and Ella are playing a game called "Guess My Rule." Ralph has kept track of his guesses and Ella's responses in this table.

Ralph	0	1	2	3	4	5	6
Ella	10	9	8	7	6	5	

Look for a pattern and predict Ella's response for the number 6. Describe this pattern.

2. Mollie is using the following chart to help her figure prices for tickets.

Tickets	1	2	3	4
Price	$7.50	$12.50	$17.50	$22.50

A customer came in and ordered 10 tickets. How much should Mollie charge for this order?

3. Brad needs to set up a coding system for files in the library using combinations of letters. He has begun this table.

Letters	1	2	3	4	5
Combinations	1	4	9	16	

How many files can Brad code using the letters A, B, C, D, and E?

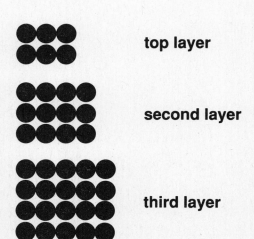

4. If the library has 400 items to code, how many letters will the librarian need to use?

5. Billie needs to make a tower of soup cans as a display in a grocery store. Each layer of the tower will be in the shape of a rectangle. The length and the width of each layer will be one less than the layer below it.

How many cans will be needed for the fifth layer of the tower?

How many cans will be needed for a 10-layer tower?

top layer

second layer

third layer

PRACTICE WORKSHEET 3-7

Dividing Decimals

Divide.

1. $6\overline{)1.38}$

2. $7\overline{)7.21}$

3. $9\overline{)0.36}$

4. $3\overline{)9.18}$

5. $0.8\overline{)6.4}$

6. $0.7\overline{)0.63}$

7. $0.3\overline{)27}$

8. $8\overline{)2}$

9. $14\overline{)0.56}$

10. $8\overline{)32.2}$

11. $5.3\overline{)0.3869}$

12. $0.8\overline{)3.76}$

13. $2.3\overline{)1.61}$

14. $7.8\overline{)0.39}$

15. $4.4\overline{)16.72}$

16. $7.9\overline{)\$41.08}$

17. $7.1\overline{)0.0426}$

18. $6.5\overline{)\$769.34}$

19. $0.83\overline{)0.1909}$

20. $7.9\overline{)0.1185}$

21. $\$0.84 \div 12$

22. $0.414 \div 3$

23. $25 \div 0.5$

24. $139.4 \div 4.1$

Solve.

25. How many nickels can Jeb get for $7.35?

26. Kara can park her car for 1 hour for 75¢. If she spends $3.00 on parking, how long does she park?

PRACTICE WORKSHEET 3-8

Scientific Notation

Write in scientific notation.

1. 860

2. 2,000

3. 7,200

4. 840,000

5. 163,000

6. 87,400

7. 2,340

8. 3 million

9. 595,000

10. 480

11. 14,380

12. 6 thousand

13. 2,540

14. 13,800

15. 352,000

16. 156

17. 4,230,000

18. 37,700

19. 5,220,000

20. 455,000

21. 25,200,000

22. 43,200

23. 20 billion

24. 4 million

Write in standard form.

25. 1.9×10^5

26. 3.7×10^3

27. 6.82×10^6

28. 1.67×10^3

29. 5.38×10^5

30. 9.73×10^4

31. 4.4×10^9

32. 2.3×10^8

33. 7.85×10^7

34. 7.65×10^5

35. 8.79×10^6

36. 4.92×10^3

37. 3.19×10^5

38. 1.5×10^9

39. 7.92×10^3

40. 2.77×10^8

41. 2×10^6

42. 6.01×10^7

PRACTICE LESSON 3-9

Geometric Sequences

Find the common ratio and write the next three terms in each geometric sequence.

1. 6, 18, 54, 162, ☐, ☐, ☐

2. 14, 28, 56, 112, ☐, ☐, ☐

3. 405, 135, 45, 15, ☐, ☐, ☐

4. 48, 24, 12, 6, ☐, ☐, ☐

5. 3, 15, 75, 375, ☐, ☐, ☐

6. 0.5, 5, 50, 500, ☐, ☐, ☐

7. 3, 6, 12, 24, ☐, ☐, ☐

8. 4, 20, 100, 500, ☐, ☐, ☐

9. 3, 12, 48, 192, ☐, ☐, ☐

10. 1.4, 2.8, 5.6, 11.2, ☐, ☐, ☐

11. 1.3, 2.6, 5.2, 10.4, ☐, ☐, ☐

12. 800, 200, 50, 12.5, ☐, ☐, ☐

13. 0.12, 0.48, 1.92, 7.68, ☐, ☐, ☐

14. 5, 5.5, 6.05, 6.655, ☐, ☐, ☐

15. 2, 12, 72, 432, ☐, ☐, ☐

16. 2.7, 8.1, 24.3, 72.9, ☐, ☐, ☐

17. 2, 3, 4.5, 6.75, ☐, ☐, ☐

18. 8.8, 4.4, 2.2, 1.1, ☐, ☐, ☐

19. 80.6, 40.3, 20.15, 10.075, ☐, ☐, ☐

20. 1.5, 12, 96, 768, ☐, ☐, ☐

21. 0.8, 2, 5, 12.5, ☐, ☐, ☐

22. 900, 450, 225, 112.5, ☐, ☐, ☐

Solve.

23. Inez is playing a video game. The longer she keeps her token active, the higher the point values become, doubling every minute. If the point value at the start was 20, what will the value be if she keeps her token active for 10 minutes?

24. Water is being lost through a leak in a tank. The hole causing the leak is widening and the water loss has been tripled each day. If 2 gallons were lost on the first day, how many gallons would be lost on the seventh day?

PRACTICE WORKSHEET 3-10

Formulas

A formula for finding the amount of work needed is W = Fd.
Find the amount of work needed.

1. $F = 12$ lb; $d = 20$ ft

2. $F = 28$ lb; $d = 150$ ft

3. $F = 90$ lb; $d = 25$ ft

4. $F = 175$ lb; $d = 20.5$ ft

5. $F = 99$ lb; $d = 5.5$ ft

6. $F = 150$ lb; $d = 50$ ft

Find the circumference of each circle. Use 3.14 for π.

7. $d = 33$ cm

8. $r = 26$ ft

9. $r = 4.2$ in.

10. $d = 7.5$ m

A formula for determining a normal blood pressure reading (B.P.) is B.P. = $110 + \dfrac{A}{2}$.
The A stands for age in years. Find the normal blood presssure
for each age.

15. 16

16. 78

17. 21

18. 35

19. 56

20. 65

21. 37

22. 75

Write a formula. Then solve.

23. The air distance from Boston, Massachusetts to San Francisco, California is about 2,700 mi. If a flight from Boston to San Francisco takes 6 h, at what rate does the plane fly?

24. The road distance from Boston to San Francisco is about 3,200 mi. To the nearest hundredth, how many hours of driving time will it take Ms. Costello if her rate is 55 mph?

25. Ms. Costello's car averages 28 miles per gallon of gasoline. To the nearest hundredth, how many gallons will be used for the drive from Boston to San Francisco?

26. If gasoline on average costs $1.35 per gallon, to the nearest cent how much will Ms. Costello spend on gasoline for the drive from Boston to San Francisco?

PRACTICE WORKSHEET 3-11

Area of Rectangles

Find the area of each rectangle.

1.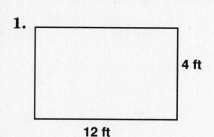
4 ft
12 ft

2.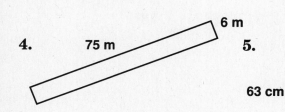
9 in.
27 in.

3.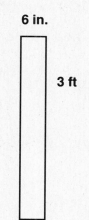
6 in.
3 ft

4. 75 m   6 m

5. 63 cm   92 cm

6. 8.5 cm   110 mm

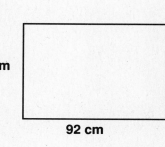
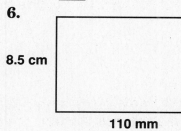

7. length, 37 km; width, 12 km

8. length, 5 in.; width, 3.5 in.

9. length, 38 in.; width, 2 ft

10. length, 18 cm; width, 6 cm

11. length, 9 cm; width, 3.5 cm

12. length, 41 feet; width, 75 feet

13. length, 18 in.; width, 2 yd

14. length, 2 km; width, 0.075 km

Solve.

15. A family room floor measures 18 feet 6 inches by 15 feet 3 inches. Find the area of the floor in square feet.

16. An expert painter with a sprayer can cover about 600 square feet of wall surface in half an hour. How long would it take an expert to paint both sides of a corridor in which each wall is 10 feet high by 90 feet long?

17. Plastic sheeting is sold in rolls that are 30 inches wide. The strip of sheeting on a roll is 75 yards long. How many square feet of sheeting are on a roll?

18. José can cut 10,000 square feet of grass in an hour. How long would it take him to cut a rectangular yard that measures 50 yards by 100 yards?

PRACTICE WORKSHEET 3-12

Statistics: Average (Mean)

Find the mean for each set of data. Round to the nearest tenth or cent.

1. 10, 10, 15, 10, 4, 1, 15

2. 59, 69, 73, 74, 61, 67, 59, 58

3. $175, $176, $172, $177, $177, $175, $175, $176, $176, $177, $173

4. 75, 80, 73, 74, 80, 80, 76, 74, 67, 70

5. 1.4, 1.5, 1.4, 1.44, 1.39, 1.48, 1.47, 1.49, 1.49, 1.42, 1.42, 1.40

6. 144, 143, 143, 138, 137, 146, 135, 141, 135, 147, 138, 134

7. 0.65, 1.62, 0.63, 1.66, 0.62, 0.65, 1.66, 0.64, 0.62, 1.62, 0.65

8. $1.60, $1.56, $1.60, $1.63, $1.59, $1.60, $1.63, $1.61, $1.58, $1.60

Solve.

9. In the first five basketball games of the season, Jojo scored 12, 15, 22, 9, and 18 points. What was Jojo's average for these five games?

10. Millen went bowling with her friends. Her scores were 182, 151, 127, and 167. What was Millen's average for these four games?

Glencoe Division, Macmillan/McGraw-Hill

PRACTICE WORKSHEET 3-13

Problem Solving: Multi-Step Problems

Solve.

1. Roy receives $45 for his birthday. He buys a new book for $7.98, a shirt for $13.99, and a puzzle game for $4.59. How much does he have left to put in his savings account?

2. Connie earns money painting house numbers on curbs. In three weeks, she earns $175, $145, and $130. She pays a supply bill of $81.30. How much does she have left?

3. Earl, Steve, and Don walk dogs for their summer spending money. They walk 5 dogs for 8 weeks and are paid $6 per week for each dog. What is each boy's share if they divide the money evenly?

4. Pat earned $22.75. Her parents gave her $20. How much more does she need to buy a sweater that costs $50?

5. Luis earns $45 each week. He saves $12.75 each week. In how many weeks will he have enough money to buy a CD player that costs $135?

6. Duwayne's lunch cost $5.35. He had a sandwich for $2.95, a drink for $0.89, and dessert. How much did dessert cost?

7. Mara works at a restaurant. She makes $3.75 an hour. She worked 20 hours and made $104.50 in tips. How much did she earn?

8. Crystal bought 2 shirts for $19.95 each and 3 pairs of socks at $3.89 a pair. Tax is $3.49. She gives the clerk three twenty-dollar bills. What is her change?

Use the passbook to find the balance on each of the following dates.

9. Sept. 15   10. Oct. 31

11. How much must Robin save to have $150?

THE CENTRAL BANK   ACCOUNT NUMBER 07-1692-03

IN ACCOUNT WITH *Robin Jeffries*

No deposits can be made or money withdrawn without presentation of this book.

DATE	INTEREST	WITHDRAWALS	DEPOSITS	BALANCE
Aug. 1	-		12 25	144 75
Aug. 20	-	45 00		
Sept. 15	-		18 35	
Oct. 31	-	1 77	19 80	

Glencoe Division, Macmillan/McGraw-Hill

PRACTICE WORKSHEET 4-1

Factors and Divisibility

Find all the factors of each number.

1. 8

2. 15

3. 21

4. 27

5. 33

6. 36

7. 42

8. 48

9. 50

10. 54

State whether each number is divisible by 2, 3, 5, 9, or 10.

11. 110

12. 225

13. 315

14. 405

15. 918

16. 243

17. 630

18. 735

19. 1,233

20. 2,460

21. 5,103

22. 8,001

23. 9,270

24. 44,127

25. 117,930

PRACTICE WORKSHEET 4-2

Prime Factorization

Write the prime factorization of each number.

1.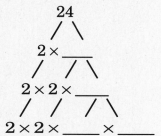

2.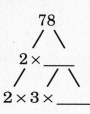

3.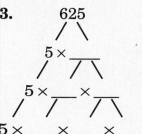

Make factor trees to express the prime factorization of each of the following. Write the prime factorization of each number.

4. 18

5. 42

6. 144

Write the prime factorization of each number.

7. 8

8. 25

9. 81

10. 100

11. 250

12. 324

13. 72

14. 156

15. 111

16. 128

17. 625

18. 550

19. 405

20. 243

21. 500

22. 512

Complete the following.

23. List the prime numbers less than 30.

24. What is the least prime factor of 221?

PRACTICE WORKSHEET 4-3

Greatest Common Factor and Least Common Multiple

Find the GCF of each group of numbers.

1. 12

27

GCF:

2. 25

30

GCF:

3. 16

24

GCF:

4. 48

60

GCF:

5. 60

75

GCF:

6. 54

72

GCF:

Find the LCM of each group of numbers.

7. 6

30

LCM:

8. 30

10

LCM:

9. 12

42

LCM:

10. 12

18

LCM:

11. 8

10

LCM:

12. 15

75

LCM:

PRACTICE WORKSHEET 4-4

Applications: Total Deductions and Take-Home Pay

Complete the chart.

	Name	Gross Pay	Total Tax Deduction	Total Personal Deduction	Take-Home Pay
1.	S. Cook	$247.80	$37.17	$35.00	
2.	R. Choi	$215.62	$29.48	$8.75	
3.	T. Brady	$195.75	$27.16	$20.00	
4.	L. Sanchez		$32.53	$9.95	$185.82
5.	F. Hyde		$35.46	$15.50	$188.48
6.	P. Morgan		$23.92	$7.25	$144.08
7.	N. Hill	$188.50		$9.40	$154.92
8.	D. Tallchief	$203.22	$25.81		$158.66
9.	R. Sanders	$217.95	$29.76		$164.19
10.	J. Ortega	$224.50		$17.50	$175.73
11.	L. Horton	$206.74	$27.44	$9.36	
12.	A. Cheng	$185.75		$5.00	$158.56
13.	T. McVay	$200.50	$24.52	$8.25	
14.	S. Shelton		$38.73	$25.00	$172.67
15.	M. Jordan	$242.83	$36.84		$187.49

Glencoe Division, Macmillan/McGraw-Hill

PRACTICE WORKSHEET 4-5

Equivalent Fractions

Replace each ☐ **with a number so that the fractions are equivalent.**

1. $\dfrac{2}{3} = \dfrac{\square}{6}$ 2. $\dfrac{3}{16} = \dfrac{\square}{48}$ 3. $\dfrac{1}{3} = \dfrac{\square}{12}$ 4. $\dfrac{6}{7} = \dfrac{\square}{49}$

5. $\dfrac{15}{20} = \dfrac{\square}{4}$ 6. $\dfrac{4}{12} = \dfrac{\square}{3}$ 7. $\dfrac{4}{16} = \dfrac{\square}{4}$ 8. $\dfrac{5}{10} = \dfrac{\square}{2}$

9. $\dfrac{3}{4} = \dfrac{\square}{12}$ 10. $\dfrac{3}{4} = \dfrac{\square}{8}$ 11. $\dfrac{1}{3} = \dfrac{\square}{6}$ 12. $\dfrac{1}{2} = \dfrac{\square}{6}$

13. $\dfrac{7}{7} = \dfrac{\square}{1}$ 14. $\dfrac{3}{7} = \dfrac{\square}{42}$ 15. $\dfrac{3}{15} = \dfrac{\square}{5}$ 16. $\dfrac{4}{32} = \dfrac{\square}{8}$

17. $\dfrac{1}{25} = \dfrac{\square}{100}$ 18. $\dfrac{7}{9} = \dfrac{\square}{18}$ 19. $\dfrac{0}{3} = \dfrac{\square}{36}$ 20. $\dfrac{6}{18} = \dfrac{\square}{3}$

21. $\dfrac{1}{3} = \dfrac{\square}{15}$ 22. $\dfrac{3}{7} = \dfrac{\square}{21}$ 23. $\dfrac{2}{5} = \dfrac{\square}{25}$ 24. $\dfrac{3}{10} = \dfrac{\square}{100}$

Name a fraction equivalent to each fraction.

25. $\dfrac{1}{3}$ 26. $\dfrac{1}{2}$ 27. $\dfrac{1}{4}$ 28. $\dfrac{3}{6}$ 29. $\dfrac{5}{8}$ 30. $\dfrac{44}{48}$

31. Write three fractions that are equivalent to $\dfrac{6}{10}$.

32. Name three fractions that are equivalent to $\dfrac{35}{100}$.

Glencoe Division, Macmillan/McGraw-Hill

PRACTICE WORKSHEET 4-6

Simplifying Fractions

Simplify.

1. $\dfrac{5}{10}$ 2. $\dfrac{4}{10}$ 3. $\dfrac{9}{12}$ 4. $\dfrac{18}{24}$

5. $\dfrac{9}{24}$ 6. $\dfrac{16}{20}$ 7. $\dfrac{13}{39}$ 8. $\dfrac{16}{48}$

9. $\dfrac{8}{16}$ 10. $\dfrac{9}{12}$ 11. $\dfrac{15}{18}$ 12. $\dfrac{5}{35}$

13. $\dfrac{20}{24}$ 14. $\dfrac{14}{16}$ 15. $\dfrac{16}{18}$ 16. $\dfrac{9}{15}$

17. $\dfrac{7}{21}$ 18. $\dfrac{6}{16}$ 19. $\dfrac{20}{36}$ 20. $\dfrac{33}{39}$

21. $\dfrac{18}{24}$ 22. $\dfrac{24}{36}$ 23. $\dfrac{32}{48}$ 24. $\dfrac{66}{121}$

25. $\dfrac{17}{34}$ 26. $\dfrac{4}{40}$ 27. $\dfrac{26}{39}$ 28. $\dfrac{20}{50}$

29. $\dfrac{25}{75}$ 30. $\dfrac{32}{80}$ 31. $\dfrac{60}{72}$ 32. $\dfrac{30}{45}$

Solve. Use the chart.

Member	Tickets sold
Ryko	73
Paul	80
Amy	75
Miguel	50
Yvonne	92
Jerome	70

33. Rank the members from 1 through 6. The one who sold the most tickets gets a rank of 1.

34. Each member had 100 tickets to sell. Write each member's sale as a fraction in simplest form.

PRACTICE WORKSHEET 4-7

Comparing Fractions

Write >, <, or = in each circle to make a true sentence.

1. $\frac{1}{3}$ ◯ $\frac{3}{4}$

2. $\frac{3}{8}$ ◯ $\frac{1}{8}$

3. $\frac{5}{6}$ ◯ $\frac{3}{7}$

4. $\frac{1}{2}$ ◯ $\frac{2}{7}$

5. $\frac{16}{20}$ ◯ $\frac{4}{5}$

6. $\frac{3}{4}$ ◯ $\frac{2}{7}$

7. $\frac{3}{5}$ ◯ $\frac{4}{5}$

8. $\frac{2}{3}$ ◯ $\frac{2}{5}$

9. $\frac{1}{3}$ ◯ $\frac{5}{7}$

10. $\frac{2}{7}$ ◯ $\frac{4}{7}$

11. $\frac{3}{16}$ ◯ $\frac{1}{8}$

12. $\frac{1}{4}$ ◯ $\frac{3}{4}$

13. $\frac{1}{6}$ ◯ $\frac{1}{7}$

14. $\frac{5}{9}$ ◯ $\frac{2}{3}$

15. $\frac{2}{11}$ ◯ $\frac{6}{33}$

16. $\frac{3}{5}$ ◯ $\frac{3}{8}$

17. $\frac{2}{7}$ ◯ $\frac{2}{5}$

18. $\frac{3}{9}$ ◯ $\frac{15}{45}$

19. $\frac{3}{5}$ ◯ $\frac{2}{3}$

20. $\frac{4}{9}$ ◯ $\frac{2}{5}$

21. $\frac{4}{5}$ ◯ $\frac{7}{10}$

22. $\frac{3}{4}$ ◯ $\frac{3}{5}$

23. $\frac{1}{3}$ ◯ $\frac{1}{4}$

24. $\frac{1}{4}$ ◯ $\frac{1}{5}$

25. $\frac{5}{6}$ ◯ $\frac{6}{7}$

26. $\frac{5}{8}$ ◯ $\frac{4}{7}$

27. $\frac{7}{8}$ ◯ $\frac{9}{10}$

28. $\frac{2}{3}$ ◯ $\frac{5}{6}$

29. $\frac{9}{10}$ ◯ $\frac{11}{12}$

30. $\frac{3}{10}$ ◯ $\frac{1}{3}$

Order the following fractions from least to greatest.

31. $\frac{2}{3}, \frac{3}{4}, \frac{1}{2}, \frac{1}{8}$

32. $\frac{1}{3}, \frac{1}{6}, \frac{1}{9}, \frac{1}{2}$

33. $\frac{5}{6}, \frac{2}{3}, \frac{3}{4}, \frac{7}{12}$

34. $\frac{2}{5}, \frac{3}{10}, \frac{1}{4}, \frac{3}{20}$

PRACTICE WORKSHEET 4-8

Mixed Numbers

Change each fraction to a mixed number in simplest form.

1. $\frac{9}{5}$ 2. $\frac{7}{6}$ 3. $\frac{19}{12}$ 4. $\frac{14}{10}$

5. $\frac{15}{9}$ 6. $\frac{7}{2}$ 7. $\frac{3}{2}$ 8. $\frac{5}{4}$

9. $\frac{9}{7}$ 10. $\frac{9}{2}$ 11. $\frac{11}{4}$ 12. $\frac{12}{5}$

13. $\frac{6}{4}$ 14. $\frac{9}{6}$ 15. $\frac{21}{15}$ 16. $\frac{55}{16}$

17. $\frac{16}{3}$ 18. $\frac{14}{5}$ 19. $\frac{24}{20}$ 20. $\frac{22}{6}$

Change each mixed number to an improper fraction.

21. $3\frac{1}{16}$ 22. $2\frac{3}{4}$ 23. $1\frac{3}{8}$ 24. $1\frac{5}{12}$

25. $7\frac{3}{5}$ 26. $6\frac{5}{8}$ 27. $3\frac{1}{3}$ 28. $1\frac{7}{9}$

29. $2\frac{3}{16}$ 30. $1\frac{2}{3}$ 31. $3\frac{3}{10}$ 32. $4\frac{3}{25}$

33. $4\frac{2}{5}$ 34. $6\frac{1}{2}$ 35. $4\frac{5}{6}$ 36. $1\frac{1}{100}$

37. $2\frac{5}{8}$ 38. $3\frac{1}{6}$ 39. $4\frac{3}{5}$ 40. $1\frac{49}{50}$

Solve.

41. How many pounds of margarine does Joel have if he has seven quarter-pound sticks?

42. How many quarters did Nancy play if she played in $2\frac{3}{4}$ basketball games?

PRACTICE WORKSHEET 4-9

Estimating Sums and Differences

Estimate.

1. $\dfrac{7}{16} + \dfrac{2}{9}$

2. $\dfrac{5}{6} + \dfrac{1}{3}$

3. $\dfrac{1}{4} - \dfrac{1}{3}$

4. $\dfrac{2}{15} + 2\dfrac{1}{20}$

5. $\dfrac{24}{25} - \dfrac{1}{2}$

6. $1\dfrac{1}{3} + \dfrac{2}{5}$

7. $\dfrac{4}{5} - \dfrac{1}{8}$

8. $\dfrac{5}{8} + \dfrac{4}{9}$

9. $3\dfrac{2}{5} - 1\dfrac{1}{4}$

10. $\dfrac{11}{12} - \dfrac{1}{3}$

11. $4\dfrac{2}{5} + \dfrac{5}{6}$

12. $6\dfrac{7}{8} - \dfrac{2}{3}$

13. $4\dfrac{7}{12} - 1\dfrac{3}{4}$

14. $9\dfrac{7}{10} + \dfrac{4}{5}$

15. $4\dfrac{2}{3} + 10\dfrac{3}{8}$

16. $18\dfrac{1}{4} - 12\dfrac{3}{5}$

17. $7\dfrac{7}{15} - 3\dfrac{1}{12}$

18. $12\dfrac{5}{9} + 8\dfrac{5}{8}$

PRACTICE WORKSHEET 4-10

Adding Fractions

Add.

1. $\dfrac{4}{7} + \dfrac{2}{7}$

2. $\dfrac{6}{9} + \dfrac{3}{9}$

3. $\dfrac{11}{15} + \dfrac{2}{15}$

4. $\dfrac{11}{15} + \dfrac{7}{15}$

5. $\dfrac{15}{20} + \dfrac{7}{20}$

6. $\dfrac{9}{11} + \dfrac{8}{11}$

7. $\dfrac{12}{20} + \dfrac{7}{20}$

8. $\dfrac{1}{5} + \dfrac{1}{4}$

9. $\dfrac{6}{7} + \dfrac{6}{7}$

10. $\dfrac{7}{10} + \dfrac{3}{5}$

11. $\dfrac{5}{8} + \dfrac{1}{4}$

12. $\dfrac{8}{15} + \dfrac{2}{3}$

13. $\dfrac{5}{12} + \dfrac{1}{3}$

14. $\dfrac{2}{3} + \dfrac{1}{6}$

15. $\dfrac{5}{6} + \dfrac{5}{18}$

16. $\dfrac{3}{5} + \dfrac{2}{3}$

17. $\dfrac{1}{2} + \dfrac{3}{7}$

18. $\dfrac{1}{2} + \dfrac{3}{8}$

19. $\dfrac{1}{6} + \dfrac{3}{5}$

20. $\dfrac{7}{8} + \dfrac{5}{6}$

21. $\dfrac{1}{12} + \dfrac{2}{5}$

22. $\dfrac{1}{8} + \dfrac{5}{6} + \dfrac{7}{12}$

23. $\dfrac{1}{2} + \dfrac{2}{3} + \dfrac{1}{6}$

Solve.

24. Paul earns $48.24 each week. He saves $\dfrac{1}{4}$ of his earnings and spends $\dfrac{2}{3}$ on clothes and school supplies. What fraction of his earnings does he set aside for savings, clothes, and school supplies?

25. In the 8th grade, $\dfrac{11}{25}$ of the students wear watches. In the 9th grade, $\dfrac{3}{5}$ of the students wear watches. In which grade do more students wear watches?

PRACTICE WORKSHEET 4-11

Adding Mixed Numbers

Add.

1. $2\frac{1}{8}$
   $+ \ 3\frac{3}{8}$

2. $5\frac{5}{6}$
   $+ \ 8\frac{1}{6}$

3. $7\frac{3}{4}$
   $+ \ 1\frac{2}{4}$

4. $8\frac{3}{8}$
   $+ \ 2\frac{7}{8}$

5. $5\frac{3}{8}$
   $+ \ 4\frac{1}{4}$

6. $7\frac{3}{5}$
   $+ \ 2\frac{1}{3}$

7. $4\frac{1}{2}$
   $+ \ 10\frac{3}{7}$

8. $9\frac{5}{6}$
   $+ \ 7\frac{2}{9}$

9. $6\frac{3}{5}$
   $+ \ 3\frac{1}{4}$

10. $8\frac{2}{3}$
    $+ \ 4\frac{5}{7}$

11. $5\frac{1}{6}$
    $+ \ 6\frac{6}{7}$

12. $3\frac{5}{8}$
    $+ \ 7\frac{1}{3}$

13. $3\frac{1}{6} + 5\frac{5}{6}$

14. $12\frac{5}{9} + 7\frac{5}{9}$

15. $2\frac{1}{8} + 1\frac{3}{5}$

16. $6\frac{3}{5} + 3\frac{1}{6}$

17. $3\frac{4}{5} + 1\frac{9}{10}$

18. $12\frac{11}{12} + 9\frac{2}{3}$

19. $9\frac{7}{8} + 8\frac{5}{6}$

20. $14\frac{7}{20} + 6\frac{4}{5}$

21. $2\frac{1}{4} + 1\frac{1}{2}$

22. $22\frac{7}{8} + 7\frac{1}{6}$

23. $15\frac{1}{2} + 4\frac{3}{4}$

24. $12\frac{4}{5} + 8\frac{5}{6}$

25. $4\frac{1}{12} + 3\frac{5}{12} + 5\frac{7}{12}$

26. $2\frac{1}{2} + 1\frac{1}{4} + \frac{1}{8}$

27. $2\frac{4}{9} + 3\frac{2}{3} + 1\frac{1}{6}$

28. $4\frac{5}{12} + 1\frac{3}{8} + 1\frac{5}{6}$

Glencoe Division, Macmillan/McGraw-Hill

PRACTICE WORKSHEET 4-12

Subtracting Fractions

Subtract.

1. $\dfrac{13}{20} - \dfrac{7}{20}$

2. $\dfrac{7}{12} - \dfrac{5}{12}$

3. $\dfrac{9}{10} - \dfrac{7}{10}$

4. $\dfrac{1}{2} - \dfrac{1}{3}$

5. $\dfrac{7}{8} - \dfrac{5}{6}$

6. $\dfrac{13}{16} - \dfrac{7}{12}$

7. $\dfrac{7}{8} - \dfrac{7}{12}$

8. $\dfrac{7}{9} - \dfrac{3}{5}$

9. $\dfrac{3}{4} - \dfrac{13}{20}$

10. $\dfrac{7}{8} - \dfrac{2}{3}$

11. $\dfrac{3}{4} - \dfrac{2}{3}$

12. $\dfrac{5}{6} - \dfrac{5}{8}$

13. $\dfrac{3}{4} - \dfrac{1}{2}$

14. $\dfrac{5}{8} - \dfrac{9}{16}$

15. $\dfrac{11}{12} - \dfrac{1}{8}$

16. $\dfrac{1}{2} - \dfrac{1}{8}$

17. $\dfrac{11}{12} - \dfrac{1}{4}$

18. $\dfrac{3}{4} - \dfrac{1}{8}$

19. $\dfrac{8}{15} - \dfrac{1}{6}$

20. $\dfrac{3}{10} - \dfrac{1}{5}$

21. $\dfrac{5}{6} - \dfrac{7}{9}$

22. $\dfrac{19}{27} - \dfrac{10}{27}$

23. $\dfrac{11}{20} - \dfrac{2}{5}$

24. $\dfrac{3}{4} - \dfrac{5}{12}$

Solve.

25. Mrs. Smith has $\dfrac{3}{4}$ gallon of milk. She uses $\dfrac{1}{2}$ gallon. How much does she have left?

26. Mr. Morales has 11 eggs. He uses $\dfrac{1}{4}$ dozen. How many dozen eggs does he have left?

PRACTICE WORKSHEET 4-13

Subtracting Mixed Numbers

Subtract.

1. $\begin{array}{r} 7\frac{3}{4} \\ -\ 6\frac{1}{4} \\ \hline \end{array}$
   2. $\begin{array}{r} 9\frac{7}{8} \\ -\ 2\frac{3}{8} \\ \hline \end{array}$
   3. $\begin{array}{r} 8 \\ -\ 6\frac{1}{5} \\ \hline \end{array}$
   4. $\begin{array}{r} 10\frac{7}{12} \\ -\ 6 \\ \hline \end{array}$

5. $\begin{array}{r} 2\frac{1}{8} \\ -\ 1\frac{1}{16} \\ \hline \end{array}$
   6. $\begin{array}{r} 12\frac{4}{5} \\ -\ 9\frac{3}{10} \\ \hline \end{array}$
   7. $\begin{array}{r} 6\frac{2}{3} \\ -\ 4\frac{1}{4} \\ \hline \end{array}$
   8. $\begin{array}{r} 7\frac{5}{6} \\ -\ 1\frac{3}{4} \\ \hline \end{array}$

9. $\begin{array}{r} 7\frac{1}{2} \\ -\ 3\frac{3}{4} \\ \hline \end{array}$
   10. $\begin{array}{r} 4\frac{7}{12} \\ -\ 2\frac{2}{3} \\ \hline \end{array}$
   11. $\begin{array}{r} 6\frac{2}{5} \\ -\ 3\frac{1}{2} \\ \hline \end{array}$
   12. $\begin{array}{r} 11\frac{1}{5} \\ -\ 7\frac{1}{3} \\ \hline \end{array}$

13. $5\frac{11}{12} - 2\frac{1}{6}$
    14. $8 - 7\frac{4}{15}$
    15. $5\frac{6}{7} - 5\frac{1}{2}$

16. $18\frac{1}{6} - 7\frac{7}{9}$
    17. $16\frac{9}{10} - 8\frac{3}{10}$
    18. $14\frac{1}{7} - 8\frac{4}{7}$

Solve.

19. After the stock rose $2\frac{3}{8}$ points, it closed at $28\frac{1}{4}$. What was the opening price?

20. Sue and Jerry are making muffins for breakfast. They need $2\frac{1}{2}$ cups of flour, but they have only $1\frac{3}{4}$ cups. How much more flour do they need?

PRACTICE WORKSHEET 4-14

Problem-Solving Strategy: Make a Drawing

Solve.

1. A loaf of bread is 10 inches long. How many cuts are necessary to cut it into 12 equal slices?

2. A floor is $6\frac{2}{3}$ feet long and $5\frac{3}{4}$ feet wide. How many 1-foot square tiles are needed to cover the floor?

3. Kima runs 5 yards every time Randy runs 4 yards. If Randy runs 24 yards, how far does Kima run?

4. Each bead on an add-a-bead necklace costs $2. How much do 6 beads cost?

5. In how many ways can you make two right triangles from an equilateral triangle with a single straight cut?

6. Every time Jennifer earns a dollar she saves $0.35. If she has earned $7, how much has she saved?

7. The Cameron family is seated at a circular table for a holiday dinner. If the third person is directly across from the ninth person, and each person is equidistant from the adjacent persons, how many people are seated at the table?

8. Mr. Gardner is building a 100-foot fence across the back of his property. If he places the fence posts 10 feet apart, how many posts will he need?

PRACTICE WORKSHEET 5-1

Estimating Products and Quotients

Estimate.

1. $4\frac{1}{3} \times 3$

2. $2\frac{1}{3} \times 1\frac{7}{8}$

3. $5\frac{7}{8} \times 3\frac{2}{3}$

4. $2\frac{1}{7} \times 3\frac{1}{6}$

5. $7\frac{2}{7} \div 1\frac{1}{3}$

6. $4\frac{2}{3} \div 1\frac{1}{6}$

7. $14\frac{5}{6} \div 3\frac{1}{3}$

8. $5\frac{1}{2} \div 2\frac{6}{7}$

9. $4\frac{2}{5} \times 3\frac{1}{7}$

10. $3\frac{3}{5} \times 1\frac{2}{7}$

11. $2\frac{2}{5} \div 1\frac{4}{5}$

12. $27\frac{1}{3} \div 9\frac{1}{3}$

13. $6\frac{7}{8} \times \frac{7}{8}$

14. $14\frac{1}{6} \div 2\frac{3}{4}$

15. $1\frac{7}{8} \div 1\frac{5}{6}$

16. $8 \times 5\frac{5}{9}$

17. $23\frac{1}{2} \div 3\frac{5}{8}$

18. $6\frac{3}{10} \times 2\frac{5}{8}$

19. $2\frac{1}{4} \times 5\frac{3}{8}$

20. $33\frac{1}{3} \div 4\frac{2}{5}$

21. $16\frac{5}{6} \div 3\frac{9}{10}$

22. $2\frac{7}{12} \times 1\frac{5}{12}$

23. $9\frac{7}{8} \times 1\frac{9}{16}$

24. $28\frac{2}{7} \div 9\frac{1}{4}$

25. Is $\frac{5}{6}$ of 3 less than or greater than 3?

26. Is $\frac{1}{3}$ of $2\frac{1}{2}$ less than, greater than, or equal to $2\frac{1}{2}$?

27. Is $\frac{3}{8}$ of $\frac{1}{2}$ less than or greater than 0?

28. Is $\frac{4}{5}$ of $1\frac{3}{4}$ less than or greater than $1\frac{3}{4}$?

29. Is $2\frac{1}{2} \div 4$ less than or greater than $2\frac{1}{2}$?

30. Is $3\frac{5}{6} \div \frac{2}{3}$ less than or greater than $3\frac{5}{6}$?

31. Is $4\frac{1}{5} \div 3\frac{1}{5}$ less than or greater than $4\frac{1}{5}$?

32. Is $8 \div 4\frac{2}{3}$ less than or greater than 8?

PRACTICE WORKSHEET 5-2

Multiplying Fractions

Multiply.

1. $\frac{1}{2} \times \frac{1}{6}$

2. $\frac{1}{3} \times \frac{1}{2}$

3. $\frac{1}{3} \times \frac{4}{9}$

4. $\frac{3}{4} \times \frac{5}{7}$

5. $\frac{2}{3} \times \frac{7}{9}$

6. $\frac{3}{5} \times \frac{4}{7}$

7. $\frac{1}{3} \times 5$

8. $6 \times \frac{1}{2}$

9. $\frac{2}{3} \times 9$

10. $\frac{7}{8} \times \frac{2}{5}$

11. $\frac{2}{3} \times \frac{3}{4}$

12. $\frac{5}{8} \times \frac{2}{5}$

13. $\frac{3}{8} \times \frac{5}{6}$

14. $\frac{3}{8} \times \frac{4}{9}$

15. $\frac{8}{9} \times \frac{3}{16}$

16. $\frac{5}{9} \times \frac{3}{5}$

17. $\frac{7}{8} \times \frac{4}{7}$

18. $\frac{15}{16} \times \frac{4}{5}$

19. $\frac{5}{6} \times \frac{3}{4}$

20. $\frac{2}{3} \times \frac{9}{10}$

21. $\frac{7}{10} \times \frac{5}{6}$

22. $\frac{4}{5} \times \frac{5}{16}$

23. $\frac{3}{10} \times \frac{6}{7}$

24. $\frac{7}{12} \times \frac{3}{14}$

25. $\frac{5}{8} \times \frac{9}{10}$

26. $\frac{7}{8} \times \frac{4}{9}$

27. $\frac{7}{10} \times \frac{15}{16}$

28. $\frac{1}{2} \times \frac{2}{3} \times \frac{3}{4}$

29. $\frac{1}{2} \times \frac{1}{3} \times \frac{4}{7}$

30. $\frac{9}{16} \times \frac{2}{3} \times \frac{5}{6}$

31. $\frac{5}{12} \times \frac{4}{5} \times \frac{3}{4}$

32. $\frac{7}{8} \times \frac{3}{14} \times \frac{7}{9}$

33. $\frac{13}{16} \times \frac{8}{9} \times \frac{2}{3}$

Solve.

34. What is $\frac{1}{2}$ of $\frac{2}{3}$ cup of sugar?

35. What is $\frac{3}{4}$ of a 3-pound box of raisins?

PRACTICE WORKSHEET 5-3

Multiplying Mixed Numbers

Multiply.

1. $2\frac{1}{8} \times 4\frac{4}{5}$

2. $2\frac{3}{4} \times 1\frac{2}{3}$

3. $1\frac{5}{8} \times 1\frac{1}{2}$

4. $6\frac{3}{10} \times 3\frac{1}{3}$

5. $3\frac{4}{5} \times 2\frac{2}{3}$

6. $2\frac{1}{10} \times 2\frac{1}{7}$

7. $1\frac{1}{5} \times 3\frac{1}{8}$

8. $5\frac{1}{2} \times 2\frac{2}{3}$

9. $6\frac{2}{3} \times 2\frac{1}{10}$

10. $2\frac{2}{7} \times 4\frac{3}{8}$

11. $2\frac{1}{2} \times 1\frac{3}{5}$

12. $3\frac{1}{2} \times 1\frac{3}{5}$

13. $4\frac{2}{3} \times 1\frac{7}{8}$

14. $3\frac{3}{4} \times 2\frac{4}{5}$

15. $7\frac{1}{3} \times 2\frac{5}{11}$

16. $3\frac{1}{2} \times 3\frac{1}{2}$

17. $1\frac{1}{5} \times 2\frac{3}{4}$

18. $1\frac{3}{5} \times 3\frac{5}{6}$

19. $3\frac{6}{10} \times 8\frac{1}{12}$

20. $4\frac{3}{7} \times 1\frac{4}{5}$

21. $3\frac{2}{3} \times 5\frac{1}{4}$

22. $6\frac{3}{7} \times 2\frac{5}{8}$

23. $3\frac{1}{5} \times 2\frac{5}{16}$

24. $4\frac{3}{5} \times 3\frac{1}{3}$

25. $2\frac{3}{4} \times \frac{2}{5} \times 8$

26. $3\frac{1}{3} \times \frac{3}{8} \times 2\frac{1}{6}$

27. $4\frac{1}{2} \times 2\frac{1}{4} \times 2\frac{2}{3}$

Solve.

28. A hose fills $\frac{5}{16}$ of a bucket in one minute. How much of a bucket will it fill in 3 minutes?

29. Gae proofread $5\frac{2}{3}$ pages in one hour. How many pages can she proofread in $7\frac{1}{2}$ hours?

PRACTICE WORKSHEET 5-4

Applications: Energy and Coal

The chart gives the energy equivalents for one year of appliance operation.

Use the chart to find the energy equivalent in tons of coal for using each appliance.

Appliance	Energy Equivalent in Tons of Coal
Range	$\frac{1}{2}$
Microwave oven	$\frac{1}{10}$
Water heater	2
Lighting a 6-room house	$\frac{1}{3}$
Refrigerator	1
Radio	$\frac{1}{20}$
Dishwasher	$\frac{1}{5}$
Color TV	$\frac{1}{4}$

1. lighting a 6-room house for 3 years

2. a range for $\frac{1}{2}$ year

3. a color TV for 3 years

4. a water heater for $\frac{1}{4}$ year

5. a microwave oven for $\frac{3}{4}$ year

6. a radio for 4 years

7. a range for 1 month

8. lighting a 6-room house for 7 months

9. a microwave oven and a dishwasher for 1 year

10. a water heater and a range for 2 years

11. a radio and a color TV for $\frac{1}{2}$ year

PRACTICE WORKSHEET 5-5

Problem-Solving Strategy: Simplifying the Problem

Solve.

On Monday, or day number 1, Sarah, Rich, and Claire heard a funny joke on the radio. These people each told the joke to 3 more people on day number 2, who each told the joke to 3 more people on day number 3. The pattern continued.

1. How many days passed before 100 people heard the joke?

2. How many people heard the joke on day 6? By the end of day 6, how many people altogether had heard the joke?

3. The summer camp has 7 buildings arranged in a circle. Paths must be constructed joining every building to every other building. How many paths are needed?

4. In a basketball tournament, each team plays until it loses a game, then it is out of the tournament. If 64 teams are in the tournament at the start, how many games must be played to determine the tournament winner?

5. Four people can unpack 24 crates in 2 hours. How many crates can 5 people unpack in 3 hours?

6. A loaf of raisin bread needs to be cut into 20 slices. How many cuts are necessary?

PRACTICE WORKSHEET 5-6

Dividing Fractions

Divide.

1. $4 \div \frac{1}{2}$

2. $\frac{4}{9} \div \frac{2}{3}$

3. $\frac{5}{6} \div 5$

4. $\frac{9}{10} \div \frac{3}{5}$

5. $\frac{8}{13} \div \frac{4}{7}$

6. $\frac{5}{12} \div \frac{10}{11}$

7. $\frac{6}{7} \div 2$

8. $\frac{2}{15} \div \frac{2}{5}$

9. $\frac{4}{7} \div \frac{8}{11}$

10. $8 \div \frac{2}{3}$

11. $\frac{3}{5} \div \frac{6}{7}$

12. $\frac{1}{9} \div \frac{5}{6}$

13. $20 \div \frac{4}{5}$

14. $\frac{2}{9} \div \frac{7}{18}$

15. $\frac{7}{11} \div \frac{21}{22}$

16. $\frac{8}{15} \div \frac{12}{25}$

17. $\frac{16}{19} \div \frac{4}{5}$

18. $\frac{5}{12} \div \frac{5}{8}$

19. $\frac{14}{17} \div \frac{21}{23}$

20. $\frac{9}{11} \div \frac{3}{4}$

21. $18 \div \frac{21}{25}$

22. $\frac{6}{13} \div 2$

23. $\frac{13}{16} \div \frac{5}{32}$

24. $\frac{11}{12} \div \frac{7}{24}$

Solve.

25. Rosa's birthday cake was cut into pieces such that each piece was $\frac{1}{32}$ of the entire cake. If $\frac{3}{4}$ of the cake was eaten, how many pieces were eaten?

PRACTICE WORKSHEET 5-7

Dividing Mixed Numbers

Divide.

1. $3 \div 1\frac{1}{3}$

2. $14 \div 1\frac{3}{4}$

3. $\frac{5}{7} \div 2\frac{1}{7}$

4. $1\frac{4}{5} \div \frac{3}{5}$

5. $4\frac{5}{6} \div 3\frac{8}{9}$

6. $2\frac{1}{4} \div 6$

7. $2\frac{4}{7} \div 1\frac{1}{4}$

8. $3\frac{1}{8} \div 4\frac{7}{8}$

9. $10\frac{2}{7} \div 6\frac{1}{7}$

10. $3\frac{5}{7} \div \frac{6}{22}$

11. $\frac{7}{15} \div 1\frac{2}{15}$

12. $3\frac{8}{9} \div 1\frac{13}{15}$

13. $12 \div 3\frac{3}{7}$

14. $2\frac{8}{9} \div \frac{3}{9}$

15. $\frac{4}{5} \div 1\frac{7}{10}$

16. $\frac{4}{5} \div 3\frac{1}{2}$

17. $2\frac{1}{3} \div 8$

18. $1\frac{1}{5} \div 2\frac{5}{8}$

19. $3\frac{3}{4} \div \frac{7}{12}$

20. $5\frac{1}{8} \div \frac{1}{6}$

21. $7\frac{2}{3} \div 6\frac{1}{2}$

22. $3\frac{1}{9} \div 6\frac{1}{9}$

23. $2\frac{6}{7} \div 6\frac{2}{5}$

24. $4\frac{1}{6} \div 2\frac{1}{2}$

25. $4\frac{4}{5} \div 4\frac{8}{9}$

26. $11\frac{1}{5} \div 3\frac{3}{5}$

27. $3\frac{3}{5} \div 9$

28. $4\frac{9}{10} \div 1\frac{1}{20}$

29. $1\frac{7}{20} \div 4\frac{3}{5}$

30. $7\frac{1}{2} \div 1\frac{5}{19}$

Solve.

31. Strips $\frac{2}{9}$ of a yard wide must be cut from $4\frac{1}{2}$ yards of fabric. How many strips can be cut?

32. In 7 ounces of fertilizer, there are $1\frac{3}{5}$ ounces phosphorus. What part of the fertilizer is phosphorus?

Glencoe Division, Macmillan/McGraw-Hill

PRACTICE WORKSHEET 5-8

Changing Fractions to Decimals

Change each fraction to a decimal. Use bar notation to show a repeating decimal.

1. $\frac{3}{4}$

2. $\frac{2}{5}$

3. $\frac{7}{8}$

4. $\frac{1}{3}$

5. $\frac{4}{9}$

6. $\frac{3}{11}$

7. $\frac{17}{20}$

8. $\frac{5}{6}$

9. $\frac{3}{16}$

10. $\frac{8}{33}$

11. $\frac{7}{12}$

12. $\frac{14}{25}$

13. $\frac{7}{10}$

14. $\frac{5}{8}$

15. $\frac{11}{15}$

16. $\frac{8}{9}$

17. $\frac{15}{16}$

18. $\frac{1}{12}$

19. $\frac{7}{20}$

20. $\frac{5}{18}$

21. $\frac{3}{10}$

22. $\frac{2}{15}$

23. $\frac{23}{50}$

24. $\frac{21}{25}$

Change each fraction to a mixed decimal.

25. $\frac{2}{3}$

26. $\frac{5}{7}$

27. $\frac{4}{11}$

28. $\frac{7}{9}$

29. $\frac{1}{6}$

30. $\frac{5}{12}$

31. $\frac{11}{30}$

32. $\frac{2}{9}$

33. $\frac{4}{15}$

PRACTICE WORKSHEET 5-9

Changing Decimals to Fractions

Change each decimal to a fraction.

1. 0.54

2. 0.06

3. 0.75

4. 0.48

5. 0.9

6. 0.005

7. 0.25

8. 0.625

9. 0.375

10. 0.4

11. 0.45

12. 0.62

13. 0.096

14. 0.357

15. 0.225

16. 0.79

17. 0.256

18. 0.08

19. 0.006

20. 0.126

21. 0.875

Change each mixed decimal to a fraction.

22. $0.55\frac{5}{9}$

23. $0.66\frac{2}{3}$

24. $0.27\frac{3}{11}$

25. $0.16\frac{2}{3}$

26. $0.57\frac{1}{7}$

27. $0.41\frac{2}{3}$

Write <, >, or = in each ◯ to make a true sentence.

28. $0.\overline{7}$ ◯ $\frac{7}{10}$

29. $\frac{3}{7}$ ◯ 0.428

30. $0.\overline{6}$ ◯ $\frac{2}{3}$

31. 0.2 ◯ $\frac{2}{9}$

32. 0.8 ◯ $\frac{4}{5}$

33. 0.83 ◯ $\frac{5}{6}$

Glencoe Division, Macmillan/McGraw-Hill

PRACTICE WORKSHEET 5-10

Problem Solving: Using Fractions

Solve. Write each fraction in simplest form.

1. XYZ stock increased $\frac{5}{8}$ one week, $\frac{3}{4}$ the second week, and $\frac{1}{8}$ the third week. What was the stock's average weekly price increase?

2. The regular price of a tennis racket is $24. What is the sale price during the "$\frac{1}{3}$-off" sale?

3. A machine is switched off and repaired because $\frac{7}{8}$ of the bolts it produced were defective. Out of 64 bolts, how many were defective?

4. There are only $2\frac{1}{4}$ yards of ribbon left on a roll. Sheila needs $\frac{1}{3}$ yard for a bow for each of 7 dolls she is making. Is there enough ribbon? If not, how much more is needed?

5. Tim has four $8\frac{1}{2}$-foot boards that he could use for shelves. He decided to make just 3 shelves from each board so that none would be wasted. How long will each shelf be?

6. Four $12\frac{7}{8}$-inch pieces of molding are needed to frame a picture. Since the color may differ a little in different molding strips, Jane wants to cut the 4 pieces from the same strip. How long must the strip be?

7. Adult shoe sizes start at size 1, which has an inside length of $8\frac{7}{12}$ inches. There is a $\frac{1}{3}$-inch difference in full sizes. How long is an adult size 5 shoe?

8. A recipe for 12 dozen muffins calls for $4\frac{1}{2}$ cups of oatmeal. Steve wants to make only six dozen muffins. How much oatmeal should he use?

PRACTICE WORKSHEET 6-1

The Metric System

Name the place value related to each prefix.

1. kilo   2. deci

3. centi   4. milli

5. hecto   6. deka

Complete. Use the place-value chart.

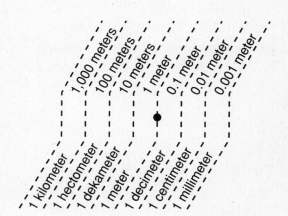

7. 1 kilometer = _____ meter(s)

8. 1 centimeter = _____ meter(s)

9. 1 millimeter = _____ meter(s)

10. 1 dekagram = _____ gram(s)

11. 1 decigram = _____ gram(s)

12. 1 hectoliter = _____ liters(s)

Name the metric unit for each measurement.

13. 0.001 liter   16. 100 meters

14. 1,000 grams   17. 10 meters

15. 0.01 gram   18. 0.1 meter

Underline the larger unit.

19. 1 decileter or centiliter   20. 1 centigram or 1 kilogram

21. 1 hectometer or 1 millimeter   22. 1 dekaliter or 1 deciliter

Glencoe Division, Macmillan/McGraw-Hill

Name _____ Date _____

PRACTICE WORKSHEET 6-2

Measuring Length

Choose the most reasonable measurement.

1. thickness of a nickel   1.5 cm   1.5 km   1.5 mm

2. width of an auditorium   33 mm   33 m   33 km

3. length of an earthworm   100 mm   100 cm   100 m

Use a metric ruler to measure each item. Give the measurement to the nearest centimeter and in millimeters.

4.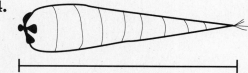

5.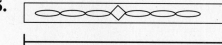

6.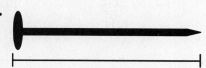

7.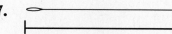

8.

9.

10.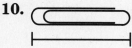

11.

Name _____ Date _____

PRACTICE WORKSHEET 6-3

Changing Metric Units

Complete.

1. 3 km = _____ m

2. 4 m = _____ mm

3. 5 mm = _____ cm

4. 20 km = _____ cm

5. 30 cm = _____ m

6. 820 mm = _____ m

7. 9 cm = _____ mm

8. 50 m = _____ cm

9. 99 m = _____ km

10. 5 m = _____ mm

11. 12 mm = _____ cm

12. 0.2 km = _____ cm

13. 39 cm = _____ m

14. 82 mm = _____ m

15. 92 cm = _____ mm

16. 1.3 m = _____ cm

17. 905 m = _____ km

18. 3.1 km = _____ m

19. 3.7 m = _____ mm

20. 50 mm = _____ cm

21. 0.9 km = _____ cm

22. 39.5 cm = _____ m

23. 132 cm = _____ m

24. 21 cm = _____ mm

25. 0.34 m = _____ cm

26. 57 m = _____ km

Solve.

27. The handlebars of Jackie's racing bike are 97 centimeters above the ground. How many millimeters is this?

28. The distance from Oak Street to Main Street is 0.75 kilometers. How many meters is this?

PRACTICE WORKSHEET 6-4

Measuring Mass

Complete.

1. 54 g = _____ mg

2. 7 kg = _____ g

3. 8.5 kg = _____ g

4. 2.7 g = _____ mg

5. 458 g = _____ kg

6. 3 mg = _____ g

7. 78 kg = _____ g

8. 3,952 g = _____ kg

9. 16 g = _____ kg

10. 41.7 g = _____ mg

11. 4,351 mg = _____ g

12. 2 g = _____ kg

13. 906 g = _____ kg

14. 38 mg = _____ g

15. 7.5 g = _____ kg

16. 6,000 g = _____ kg

17. 520 mg = _____ g

18. 25,480 g = _____ kg

Solve.

19. The King High School yearbook has a mass of 520 grams. If 430 students ordered the yearbook, what is the mass in kilograms of all these yearbooks combined?

20. Sandy weighed the newspapers that she delivered last Sunday. They weighed 75 kilograms in all. If Sandy delivered 62 Sunday papers, about how much did one paper weigh?

21. The total weight of 3 kittens is 8.7 kilograms. What is the average weight of each kitten in grams?

22. One egg weighs about 35 grams. About how much do a dozen eggs weigh in kilograms?

Glencoe Division, Macmillan/McGraw-Hill

PRACTICE WORKSHEET 6-5

Measuring Capacity

Complete.

1. 2 kL = _____ L

2. 5 L = _____ mL

3. 125 mL = _____ L

4. 0.52 kL = _____ L

5. 12.4 kL = _____ L

6. 15 L = _____ kL

7. 75 mL = _____ L

8. 309 mL = _____ L

9. 900 L = _____ kL

10. 0.06 L = _____ mL

11. 85 kL = _____ L

12. 3,500 L = _____ kL

13. 425 L = _____ kL

14. 29.3 L = _____ mL

15. 0.25 L = _____ mL

16. 0.4 kL = _____ L

17. 32 L = _____ mL

18. 51.3 L = _____ kL

Solve.

19. The social committee figures it needs one 180-milliliter serving of punch for each of the 140 guests at the reception. How many liters of punch do they need in all?

20. The Adams family car has a gas tank with a capacity of 50 liters. After a trip they filled the tank with 42 liters of gas. How much gas was in the tank before they filled it?

21. Seventeen people attended the Forbes family picnic. They had 10 liters of lemonade at the start, and it was all gone at the end of the day. If each person had an equal amount of lemonade, about how many milliliters did each drink?

22. The daily dosage of medicine for Joe's allergy is 2 milliliters. The bottle contained 0.24 liter when it was full. How many days will this medicine last?

Glencoe Division, Macmillan/McGraw-Hill

PRACTICE WORKSHEET 6-6

Problem-Solving Strategy: Acting It Out

Solve.

1. Twenty votes were cast for club president. You won by 4 votes over your opponent. How many votes did you receive?

2. For every $3 your friend earned, you earned $5. How much did you earn if your friend earned $12?

3. You have 4 different-colored bangle bracelets. How many different combinations of 2 or 3 bracelets can you wear?

4. Sue is shorter than Tom and taller than Bob. Tom is taller than Bob and shorter than Amy. Put the people in order from tallest to shortest.

5. Sam has more money than Sue. Allen has less money than Sue. Does Sam have more money than Allen?

6. Four people are going out to dinner. How many different ways can the people be seated at a square table if one person only sits on each side and one person never moves?

7. There are 5 people. How many different committees of 3 people each can be formed?

8. Joan lives next door to Bob. Bob lives next door to Joe. Does Joan live next door to Joe?

PRACTICE WORKSHEET 6-7

Customary Units of Length

Complete.

1. 3 mi = _____ ft

2. 4 yd = _____ ft

3. 21 ft = _____ yd

4. 72 in. = _____ ft

5. 9 mi = _____ yd

6. 840 in. = _____ ft

7. 1 mi = _____ in.

8. 84 in. = _____ yd

9. 90 ft = _____ in.

10. 2 ft = _____ in.

11. 5 yd = _____ in.

12. 12 mi = _____ ft

13. 13 mi = _____ yd

14. 39 yd = _____ ft

15. 72 in. = _____ yd

16. 96 in. = _____ ft

17. $1\frac{1}{3}$ ft = _____ in.

18. 95 mi = _____ yd

19. 7,040 yd = _____ mi

20. $3\frac{1}{2}$ mi = _____ ft

21. 54 in. = _____ ft

22. $\frac{1}{2}$ mi = _____ ft

23. 42 ft = _____ yd

24. 132 yd = _____ ft

25. 26,436 ft = _____ mi _____ ft

26. 4,368 in. = _____ yd _____ ft

Solve.

27. The track around the field is 440 yards long. How many laps must be run to cover one mile?

28. Marco's favorite shot in basketball is 15 feet from the basket. How many inches is that?

PRACTICE WORKSHEET 6-8

Customary Units of Weight and Capacity

Complete.

1. 2 T = _____ lb

2. 16,000 lb = _____ T

3. 48 oz = _____ lb

4. 1.5 lb = _____ oz

5. 6 lb = _____ oz

6. 3 T = _____ lb

7. 3 lb 4 oz = _____ oz

8. $2\frac{1}{2}$ T = _____ lb

9. $\frac{3}{4}$ lb = _____ oz

10. 8 qt = _____ gal

11. 3 pt = _____ c

12. 12 c = _____ pt

13. 5 pt = _____ qt

14. 4 gal = _____ qt

15. 18 qt = _____ c

16. 64 fl oz = _____ qt

17. $2\frac{3}{4}$ gal = _____ pt

18. $\frac{1}{2}$ c = _____ fl oz

Solve.

19. Darwin is buying fruit juice for a party. A 32-fluid-ounce bottle costs $1.19. How much will it cost for 20 one-cup servings?

20. An 8-ounce package of ground beef costs $1.12. How much will it cost for a pound and a half of ground beef?

PRACTICE WORKSHEET 6-9

Formulas and Temperature

Choose the better temperature.

1. drinking water, 5°C or 45°C

2. a summer day, 25°C or 75°C

3. hot chocolate, 50°F or 105°F

4. a fall day, −12°C or 12° C

5. snow, ⁻42°F or 30°F

6. a comfortable room, 68°F or 20°F

7. a baking oven, 205°C or 500°C

8. a car's engine at high speed, 90°C or 32°C

Find the equivalent temperature to the nearest degree.

9. 7°C

10. 35°C

11. 272°C

12. 58°C

13. 163°C

14. 118°C

15. 54°C

16. 67°C

17. 12°C

Find the equivalent temperature to the nearest degree.

18. 59°F

19. 93°F

20. 446°F

21. 26°F

22. 84°F

23. 41°F

24. 72°F

25. 122°F

26. 107°F

Solve.

27. Would you need to wear a sweater if the room temperature was 25°C?

28. Would you need to turn on the heater in the car if the temperature was 5°C?

29. The noon temperature was reported at 83°F. The 6:00 P.M. temperature was 57°F. What was the drop in temperature?

30. A Canadian recipe called for an oven temperature of 230°C. About what temperature would this be in degrees Fahrenheit?

Glencoe Division, Macmillan/McGraw-Hill

PRACTICE WORKSHEET 6-10

Measuring Time

Complete.

1. 45 min = _____ s

2. 4 d = _____ min

3. 72 h = _____ d

4. 3 h = _____ min

5. 8 h = _____ s

6. 7 d = _____ min

7. 75 min = ____ h ____ min

8. 8 h 20 min = _____ min

9. 15 h = _____ min

10. 8 d = _____ h

11. 3,000 min = ____ d ____ h

12. 10,080 s = ____ h ____ min

Find the elapsed time.

13. from 7:15 A.M. to 10:36 A.M.

14. from 2:48 P.M. to 9:16 P.M.

15. from 3:15 P.M. to noon

16. from midnight to 5:57 A.M.

17. from 8:40 A.M. to 5:30 P.M.

18. from 9:45 P.M. to 7:50 A.M.

Solve.

19. Bill punched the time clock at the factory at 7:55 A.M. He worked for 8 hours and 25 minutes and had a 45-minute lunch break. What time did he punch out?

20. Lorie worked six days last week. She worked 7 hours and 15 minutes each day. She gets paid overtime for time worked over 40 hours in a week. How much overtime did she work?

PRACTICE WORKSHEET 6-11

Applications: Time Cards

Compute the working hours for each day.

1.
IN	OUT
7:00	11:00
12:00	16:00

2.
IN	OUT
9:30	12:30
13:00	16:30

3.
IN	OUT
8:45	12:15
13:15	16:15

4.
IN	OUT
9:00	11:50
12:30	17:00

5.
IN	OUT
7:50	11:30
12:15	17:05

6.
IN	OUT
10:35	14:00
14:30	19:15

7.
IN	OUT
7:45	11:45
12:15	16:45

8.
IN	OUT
13:30	16:45
17:15	21:20

9.
IN	OUT
8:25	12:00
12:45	17:15

10.
IN	OUT
12:20	16:15
16:45	21:30

11.
IN	OUT
7:15	11:30
12:15	16:00

12.
IN	OUT
11:50	17:05
17:45	20:15

Solve.

13. Michael's time card showed IN times of 8:30 and 12:45 and OUT times of 12:05 and 16:55 for Tuesday. If Michael earns $5.25 an hour, how much did he earn on Tuesday?

14. Stacy gets paid overtime for any hours worked over 8 hours in a day. On Friday Stacy's time card showed IN times of 7:55 and 13:05 and OUT times of 12:00 and 17:30. Did Stacy work overtime on Friday? If, so how much overtime?

PRACTICE WORKSHEET 6-12

Problem Solving: Using Measurements

Solve.

1. Marshall's flight is scheduled to leave Dallas at 8:46 A.M. and arrive at Chicago at 12:30 P.M. How long is the flight?

2. Six tablecloths, each 150 centimeters long, are needed to cover a row of picnic tables that have been placed end-to-end. About how many meters long is the row of tables?

3. On a trip, Fred bought gasoline three times — 18 gallons, 14.5 gallons, and 16.5 gallons. What was the total cost at $1.12 per gallon?

4. If each banana has a mass of about 225 g, how much will you have to pay for 6 bananas at 64¢ per kilogram?

5. On the first four days of her vacation, Carrie drove 215 miles, 360 miles, 280 miles, and 155 miles. What was the average daily distance?

6. The weather forecast is for a low overnight of 7°C and a high tomorrow of 16°C. How many degrees will the temperature have to rise?

7. You have a bad cough for which the doctor has given you medicine. The prescribed dosage is 5 milliliters, 4 times a day. How many milliliters must be in the bottle if there is enough for 1 week?

8. You are driving a truck loaded with bales of straw over a country road. The bridge you have crossed has posted a limit of 5 tons. Your truck weighs about 5,000 pounds and each of the 80 bales of straw weighs about 50 pounds. Is it safe for you to cross the bridge? What is the greatest number of bales you can safely haul across the bridge?

PRACTICE WORKSHEET 7-1

Basic Terms of Geometry

Use symbols to name the line segment between each pair of cities in as many ways as possible.

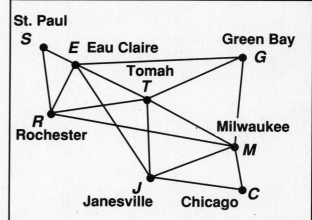

St. Paul
S

E Eau Claire

Green Bay
G

Tomah
T

R
Rochester

Milwaukee
M

J
Janesville

Chicago
C

1. Rochester and Tomah

2. Chicago and Milwaukee

3. Eau Claire and Green Bay

4. St. Paul and Rochester

Name two other real-life models for each figure.

5. point: pencil tip

6. ray: flashlight beam

7. line segment: pencil

8. part of a plane: desktop

Use symbols to name each figure in the drawing at the right.

9. 12 rays

10. 6 line segments

B

C

O

D

A

Use words and symbols to name each figure in as many ways as possible.

11.

S

R

12.

J

K

13.

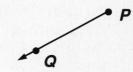

P

Q

PRACTICE WORKSHEET 7-2

Measuring Angles

Measure each angle shown in the figure at the right.

1. ∠ AND

2. ∠ END

3. ∠ GNB

4. ∠ FNE

5. ∠ GNA

6. ∠ HND

7. ∠ FNB

8. ∠ CNF

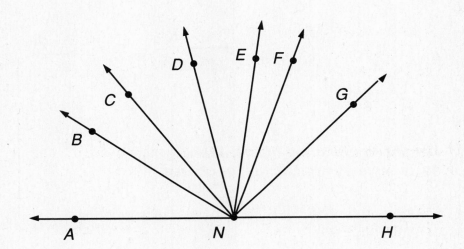

Measure each angle in triangle A and triangle B.

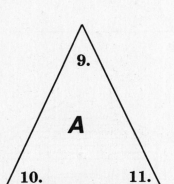

9. _____

10. _____

11. _____

12. _____

13. _____

14. _____

Make a drawing of each angle.

15. 45°

16. 30°

17. 105°

Name _____ Date _____

PRACTICE WORKSHEET 7-3

Classifying Angles

Classify each angle as right, acute, or obtuse.

1.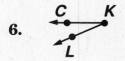

2.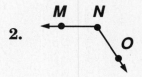

3.

4.

5.

6.

7.

8.

Use the figure at the right to classify each angle as right, acute, or obtuse.

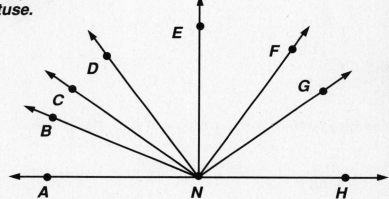

9. ∠AND

10. ∠BNF

11. ∠GND

12. ∠ANF

13. ∠DNH

14. ∠ENF

15. ∠CND

16. ∠ENC

17. ∠GNE

18. ∠HNB

Use the drawings at the right to complete the following.

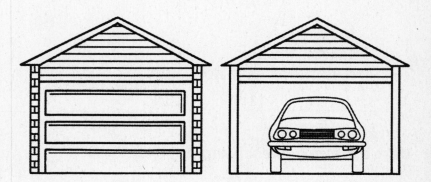

19. Find four examples of right angles. Mark their sides on the drawings, and label these angles *R*.

20. Find two examples of acute angles. Mark their sides on the drawings, and label these angles *A*.

21. Find five examples of obtuse angles. Mark their sides on the drawings, and label these angles *O*.

Glencoe Division, Macmillan/McGraw-Hill

PRACTICE WORKSHEET 7-4

Applications: Congruent Figures and Constructions

Construct a line segment congruent to each line segment. Then bisect each line segment.

1.

2.

Construct an angle congruent to each angle.

3.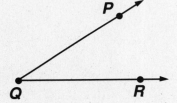

4.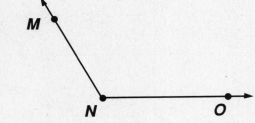

5.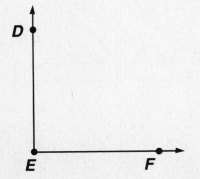

Name _____   Date _____

PRACTICE WORKSHEET 7-5

Parallel and Perpendicular Lines

State whether each pair of lines is parallel, perpendicular, *or* skew.
Use symbols to name all parallel and perpendicular lines.

1.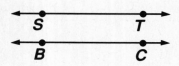

2.

3.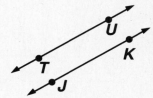

4.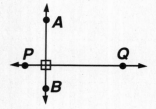

5.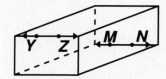

6.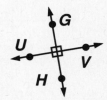

Use symbols to name the figures in each drawing.

7. all pairs of parallel lines

8. all pairs of perpendicular lines

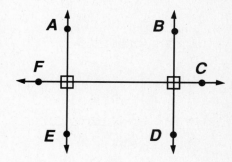

9. all line segments parallel to $\overline{LM}$

10. all line segments perpendicular to $\overline{OP}$

11. all line segments skew to $\overline{QP}$

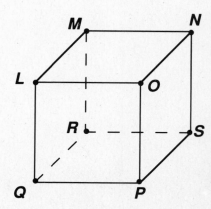

Glencoe Division, Macmillan/McGraw-Hill

Name _____ **Date** _____

PRACTICE WORKSHEET 7-6

Polygons

Complete the chart.

	Name	Prefix	Number of Sides	Number of Angles
1.			3	
2.				4
3.	pentagon			
4.		hexa-		
5.			8	
6.				10

Draw an example of each polygon.

7. not regular decagon

8. not regular pentagon

9. regular quadrilateral

10. regular hexagon

Name each by the number of sides. Then state whether it is regular or not regular.

11.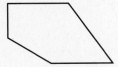

12.

13.

14.

15.

16.

Glencoe Division, Macmillan/McGraw-Hill

PRACTICE WORKSHEET 7-7

Triangles

Classify each triangle by its sides and then by its angles.

1.   **2.**   **3.** 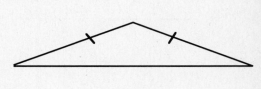   **4.**

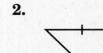

Draw an example of each triangle.

5. equilateral triangle   **6.** isosceles triangle   **7.** scalene triangle

8. acute triangle   **9.** right triangle   **10.** obtuse triangle

11. Measure the three angles of each of the triangles you drew in Exercises 5–10. What is the sum of the measures of the angles for each triangle? What conclusion would you make?

PRACTICE WORKSHEET 7-8

Quadrilaterals

Classify each quadrilateral.

1.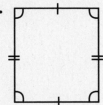
2.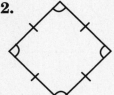
3.
4.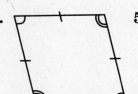
5.

State whether each statement is true or false.

6. All trapezoids are parallelograms.

7. Some quadrilaterals are squares.

8. Some rhombuses are squares.

9. Some rectangles are squares.

10. Every parallelogram is a rectangle.

11. Not every quadrilateral is a parallelogram.

Use the quadrilaterals below to complete Exercises 12 and 13.

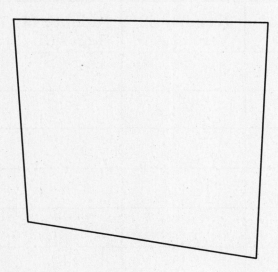

12. Measure and record the measure of each angle of both quadrilaterals.

13. What is the sum of the measures of the angles of each quadrilateral?

Glencoe Division, Macmillan/McGraw-Hill

PRACTICE WORKSHEET 7-9

Three-Dimensional Figures

Name each shape.

1.

2.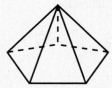

3.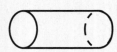

4.

Make a drawing of each three-dimensional figure.

5. rectangular pyramid   6. cone   7. hexagonal prism

Copy and complete.

	Polyhedron	Number of Faces (F)	Number of Vertices (V)	Number of Edges (E)
8.	Rectangular Prism			
9.	Triangular Pyramid			
10.	Hexagonal Prism			
11.	Rectangular Pyramid			
12.	Hexagonal Pyramid			
13.	Triangular Prism			
14.	Octagonal Prism			
15.	Octagonal Pyramid			

PRACTICE WORKSHEET 7-10

Problem – Solving Strategy: Use Logical Reasoning

Which one does not belong? Explain your answer.

1.
   a. **b.** **c.** **d.**

2.
   a. **b.** **c.** **d.**

3. **a.** vertex **b.** face
   c. ray **d.** edge

4. **a.** rhombus **b.** rectangle
   c. scalene triangle **d.** obtuse triangle

Choose the letter of the best answer. Explain your answer.

5. line segment is to ruler as angle is to
   a. triangle **b.** compass **c.** protractor **d.** ray

6. triangle is 180° as quadrilateral is to
   a. 360° **b.** 90° **c.** 180° **d.** 400°

7. prism is to parallellogram as pyramid is to
   a. point **b.** triangle **c.** base **d.** vertex

8. line is to ray as line segment is to
   a. line **b.** ray **c.** point **d.** angle

PRACTICE WORKSHEET 8-1

Circumference of Circles

Find the circumference of each circle described below. Use 3.14 for π. *Round decimal answers to the nearest tenth.*

1.

12 in.

2.

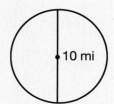

10 mi

3.

5 km

4.

8 m

5.

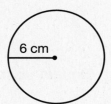

6 cm

6.

13 ft

7. $d = 4.5$ cm

8. $r = 15$ yd

9. $d = 9$ ft

10. $r = 12$ in.

11. $d = 15$ in.

12. $r = 50$ km

13. $d = 33$ m

14. $r = 5$ mm

15. $d = 20$ mi

Solve.

16. The West High School band is planning a formation for their halftime performance. They want to make a large circle with a diameter of 30 yards. If the 50 band members will be equally spaced, how many feet of circumference should there be between two consecutive positions?

17. The garden at Central City Park has a large circular fountain in the center. The radius of the circle is 27 feet. The tiles outlining the fountain are 9 inches long. How many tiles are needed to complete the outline of the fountain?

18. The diameter of the earth is about 8,000 miles. What is the circumference of the earth?

19. Suppose it were possible to string a wire around the earth's equator at a constant 100 feet above the earth. How much wire would be needed?

PRACTICE WORKSHEET 8-2

Area of Parallelograms

Find the area of each parallelogram.

1.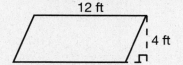
12 ft
4 ft

2.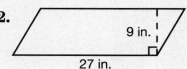
9 in.
27 in.

3.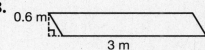
0.6 m
3 m

4.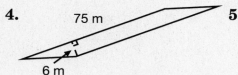
75 m
6 m

5.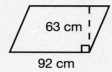
63 cm
92 cm

6.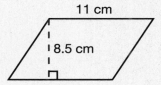
11 cm
8.5 cm

7. base, 37 km
height, 12 km

8. base, 5 in.
height, 3.5 in.

9. base, 9 cm
height, 3.8 cm

10. base, 41 ft
height, 75 ft

11. base, 1.5 ft
height, 4.5 ft

12. base, 2 km
height 0.075 km

Solve.

13. What is the area of a parallelogram with a base of 38 in. and a height of 4 in.?

14. If the height of a parallelogram is 6 cm and the base is 18 cm, what is its area?

15. A parallelogram with an area of 180 square feet has a height of 6 feet. How long is the base?

16. A parallelogram with a base of 4.2 meters has an area of 31.5 square meters. What is its height?

Glencoe Division, Macmillan/McGraw-Hill

PRACTICE WORKSHEET 8-3

Area of Triangles

Find the area of each triangle.

1.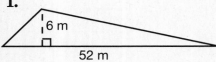
6 m
52 m

2.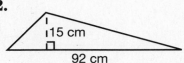
15 cm
92 cm

3.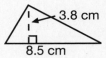
3.8 cm
8.5 cm

4.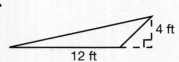
4 ft
12 ft

5.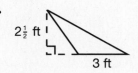
$2\frac{1}{2}$ ft
3 ft

6.
2 mi
3 mi

7. base, 6 km
height, 5 km

8. base, 4.4 in.
height, 3.5 in.

9. base, $\frac{2}{3}$ yd
height, 1 yd

10. base, 24 mm
height, 13 mm

11. base, 5 mi
height, 4 mi

12. base, $3\frac{2}{3}$ yd
height, $1\frac{2}{3}$ yd

Solve.

13. A house has a triangular-shaped section of roof that measures 21 feet at the base and has a height of 14 feet. How many square feet of roofing will be needed for this section of roof?

14. Jack is making a tent from a pattern. Both ends are shaped like a triangle that has a base of 8 feet and a height of 6 feet, including excess for hems. How many square feet of material will Jack use for the ends?

15. A triangular-shaped section of lawn measures 15 meters at the base and has a height of 8 meters. How many square meters of grass is this?

16. One section of town is bordered by three streets, forming a triangle that measures 6 kilometers at the base and has a height of 4 kilometers. How many square kilometers are contained in this section of town?

PRACTICE WORKSHEET 8-4

Area of Circles

Find the area of each circle whose radius is given. Use 3.14 for π. Round decimal answers to the nearest tenth.

Find the area of each circle whose diameter is given. Use 3.14 for π. Round decimal answers to the nearest tenth.

1. 12 in

2. 15 cm

7. 56 m

8. 4 in.

3. 5 m

4. 2.6 ft

9. 12 ft

10. 9 cm

5. 18 yd

6. 80 mm

11. 2.8 km

12. 40 mi

Find the area of each circle described below. Use 3.14 for π. Round decimal answers to the nearest tenth.

13.

18 m

14.
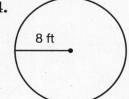
8 ft

15.

7 mm

16.
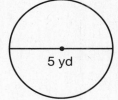
5 yd

Solve.

17. A circular fountain in Washington Park has a radius of 6 meters. How many square meters of tile are needed for the bottom of the fountain?

18. A reading room at the library is circular in shape, with a diameter of 28 feet. How many square feet of carpet are needed for this room?

19. An old mansion has a large window in the shape of a semicircle. If the bottom edge is 8 feet long, what is the area of the window?

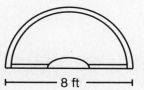
8 ft

20. A sprinkler is set up at the corner of a building and is set to spray a radius of 14 meters. How many square meters of grass will the sprinkler cover?

14 m
Sprinkler
Building

PRACTICE WORKSHEET 8-5

Applications: Installing Carpets

Find the total cost of carpeting each of the rooms pictured below. The cost per square yard of the carpeting is given.

1.

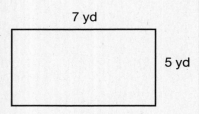

7 yd

5 yd

$14.50 per square yard

2.

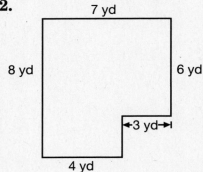

7 yd

8 yd   6 yd

◄3 yd►

4 yd

$19.95 per square yard

3.

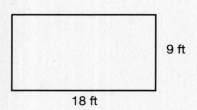

9 ft

18 ft

$17.00 per square yard

4.

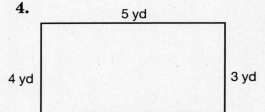

5 yd

4 yd   3 yd

1 yd

$16.99 per square yard

5.

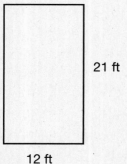

21 ft

12 ft

$21.50 per square yard

6.

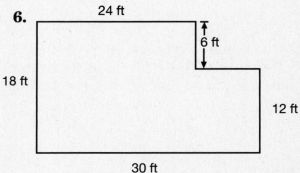

24 ft

6 ft

18 ft

12 ft

30 ft

$18.00 per square yard

PRACTICE WORKSHEET 8-6

Problem-Solving Strategy: Making a Diagram

Solve by making a diagram.

1. Darryl, Marcia, and José each work out at Sam's Gym. Darryl works out once every 2 days, Marcia every 3 days, and José every 5 days. If they are all at the gym on March 4, what is the next date they will all be at the gym?

2. It takes 5 minutes for the director to call 3 choir members and tell them the rehearsal is canceled. It takes 5 minutes for those choir members to call another 3 members each, and so on. How many choir members can be called in 20 minutes?

3. Of the 90 members of the freshman class, $\frac{1}{2}$ participate in sports and $\frac{3}{5}$ participate in music activities. If $\frac{1}{3}$ do not participate in sports or music, how many participate in both sports and music?

4. A gardener divides his seedlings equally among 5 gardens. In one garden he plants $\frac{3}{4}$ of the seedlings as a border and has 8 seedlings left over. How many seedlings did he start with?

5. A car is available in white, black, or gray; with an automatic or manual transmission; and with 2 doors or 4 doors. In how many different combinations of color, transmission, and doors is this car available?

6. Hassan used part of his savings to buy a tape player for $199.95, a compact disc player for $254.99, and speakers for $175.50. He paid sales tax of $31.52 and still had $\frac{1}{3}$ of his savings left. How much were Hassan's savings before he made these purchases?

PRACTICE WORKSHEET 8-7

Surface Area of Rectangular Prisms

Find the surface area of each rectangular prism.

1.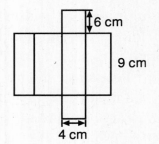
6 cm
9 cm
4 cm

2.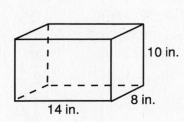
10 in.
8 in.
14 in.

3.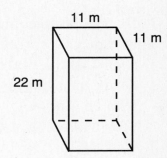
11 m
11 m
22 m

4.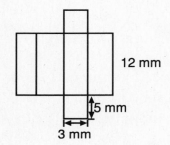
100 cm
50 cm

5.
60 cm
12 mm
5 mm
3 mm

6.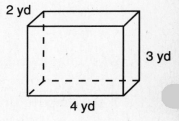
2 yd
3 yd
4 yd

7. length = 3 ft
width = 2 ft
height = 8 ft

8. length = 16 cm
width = 4 cm
height = 9 cm

9. length = 9 in.
width = 5 in.
height = 27 in.

10. length = 8 m
width = 8 m
height = 6 m

11. length = 8 yd
width = 2 yd
height = 4 yd

12. An artist made a large sculpture in the shape of a rectangular prism. It was 8 ft long by 3 ft wide by 5 ft high. What was its surface area?

13. The 8 ft by 5 ft sides of the sculpture were painted red. The 3 ft by 8 ft sides were painted blue, and the other sides were painted white. How many square feet were painted each color?

PRACTICE WORKSHEET 8-8

Surface Area of Cylinders

Find the surface area of each cylinder. Use 3.14 for π. Round decimal answers to the nearest tenth.

1.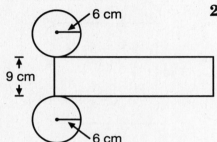
6 cm
9 cm
6 cm

2.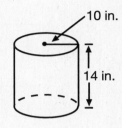
10 in.
14 in.

3.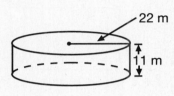
22 m
11 m

4.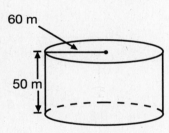
60 m
50 m

5.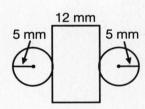
12 mm
5 mm 5 mm

6.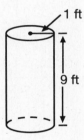
1 ft
9 ft

7. radius = 3 ft
   height = 8 ft

8. radius = 16 cm
   height = 9 cm

9. radius = 9 in.
   height = 27 in.

10. radius = 8 m
    height = 6 m

11. radius = 8 yd
    height = 4 yd

12. radius = 4 m
    height = 6.5 m

PRACTICE WORKSHEET 8-9

Volume of Rectangular Prisms

Find the volume of each rectangular prism described below.

1.
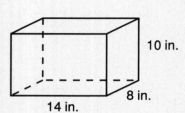
10 in.
14 in.
8 in.

2.
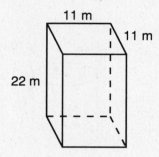
11 m
11 m
22 m

3.
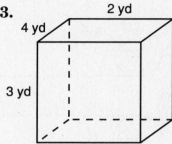
2 yd
4 yd
3 yd

4.
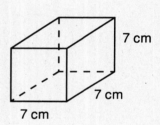
7 cm
7 cm
7 cm

5.
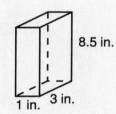
8.5 in.
1 in.   3 in.

6.
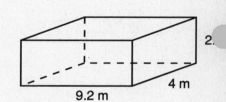
2.
9.2 m   4 m

7. $l = 12$ ft
$w = 8$ ft
$h = 7$ ft

8. $l = 5.2$ mm
$w = 12$ mm
$h = 4$ mm

9. $l = 26$ cm
$w = 19$ cm
$h = 21$ cm

10. $l = 4$ in.
$w = 17$ in.
$h = 3$ in.

11. $l = 1.3$ m
$w = 7$ m
$h = 2$ m

12. $l = 4$ yd
$w = 4$ yd
$h = 6$ yd

PRACTICE WORKSHEET 8-10

Volume of Pyramids

Find the volume of each pyramid.

1.
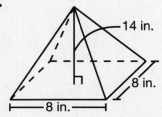
14 in.
8 in.
8 in.

2.
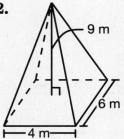
9 m
6 m
4 m

3.
8 cm
12 cm
12 cm

4.
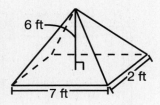
6 ft
2 ft
7 ft

5.
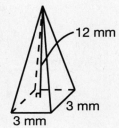
12 mm
3 mm
3 mm

6.
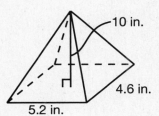
10 in.
4.6 in.
5.2 in.

7. $l = 12$ ft
$w = 12$ ft
$h = 7$ ft

8. $l = 5.8$ m
$w = 4$ m
$h = 9$ m

9. $l = 9$ in.
$w = 9$ in.
$h = 16$ in.

10. $l = 8$ m
$w = 3$ m
$h = 11$ m

11. $l = 13$ cm
$w = 7.5$ cm
$h = 10$ cm

12. $l = 15$ mm
$w = 15$ mm
$h = 17$ mm

PRACTICE WORKSHEET 8-11

Volume of Cylinders

Find the volume of each cylinder. Use 3.14 for π. Round decimal answers to the nearest tenth.

1.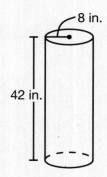
8 in.
42 in.

2.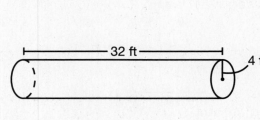
32 ft
4 ft

3.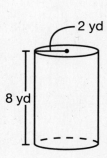
2 yd
8 yd

4.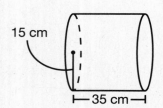
15 cm
35 cm

5.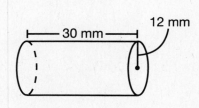
30 mm
12 mm

6.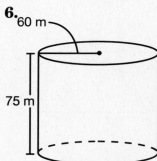
60 m
75 m

7. radius, 10 ft
   height, 8 ft

8. radius, 5 cm
   height, 19 cm

9. diameter, 14 m
   height, 9 m

10. radius, 9 in.
    height, 27 in.

11. diameter, 16 yd
    height, 11 yd

12. radius, 6 m
    height, 57 m

PRACTICE WORKSHEET 8-12

Volume of Cones

Find the volume of each cone described below. Round decimal answers to the nearest tenth.

1.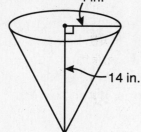

2.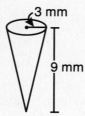

3.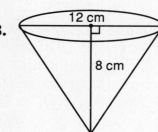

4.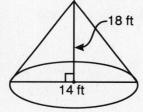

5.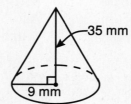

6.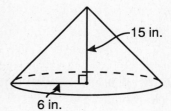

7. radius, 12 ft
   height, 8 ft

8. diameter, 28 m
   height, 9 m

9. radius, 10 in.
   height, 25 in.

10. diameter, 16 yd
    height, 11 yd

11. diameter, 10 cm
    height, 5 cm

12. radius, 27 cm
    height, 19 cm

Glencoe Division, Macmillan/McGraw-Hill

PRACTICE WORKSHEET 8-13

Problem Solving: Using Area and Volume

Solve. Round decimal answers to the nearest tenth.

1. Rita is planting English ivy. She needs 6 plants to cover 10 square feet of ground. How many plants does she need to cover a rectangular area 20 feet long and 15 feet wide?

2. Twelve boxes of detergent are to be placed in a carton. Each box is 8 in. by 3 in. by 11 in. How much space must the carton contain? Give possible dimensions of the carton.

3. A circular swimming pool is to be dug It is to have a diameter of 20 ft and a depth of 6 ft. How much dirt must be removed?

4. The weather service issued a severe storm warning for all counties within a 50-mile radius of Plainview. What is the area covered by the warning?

5. A cord of wood is equivalent to 128 cubic feet and is usually described as 4 ft by 4 ft by 8 ft. Herman helps his dad cut wood, which they sell. They have a stack 16 ft by 16 ft by 12 ft. How may cords of wood do they have ready for sale?

6.

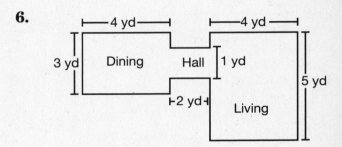

The dining, living, and hall areas are to be carpeted. How much will it cost if the carpet is priced at 412.89 per square yard?

PRACTICE WORKSHEET 9-1

Ratio

Write each ratio as a fraction in simplest form.

1. 6 losses to 13 wins

2. 4 inches of snow in 9 days

3. 21 wins to 14 losses

4. 15 children out of 60 passengers

5. 12 losses in 52 games

6. 24 passengers in 8 cars

7. 18 tickets for $54

8. 27 wins to 18 losses

9. 32 wins in a total of 80 games

10. 144 bottles in 36 cartons

11. 47 women out of 94 adults

12. 360 miles in 6 hours

Andy Peabody works for Widgets, Inc. Use his check stub to write a ratio that compares the following. (Do not write in simplest form.)

13. overtime hours to regular hours

14. FICA tax to gross pay

15. total deductions to gross pay

16. United Fund to take-home pay

Widgets, Inc.		Andy Peabody
Check Number	Tax Deductions	
12546	Federal Tax	State Tax
Pay Period	41.40	6.38
Ending	FICA	City Tax
2/14	22.38	3.27
Regular Hours		
80.0	Other Deductions	
Overtime	Union Dues	Insurance
Hours	10.00	5.20
2.5	United Fund	Bonds
	2.00	8.00
Gross Pay	Total Deductions	Take-Home Pay
334.02	100.63	233.39

Solve.

17. Bolton High School's basketball team has won 12 games and lost 6 games. What is their ratio of games won to games lost?

18. Brandon got 12 problems correct and 3 problems wrong on today's quiz. What was his ratio of problems correct to the total number of problems?

Glencoe Division, Macmillan/McGraw-Hill

PRACTICE WORKSHEET 9-2

An Introduction to Probability

A date is chosen at random from the month of February.
Find the probability of choosing each date.

February						
S	**M**	**T**	**W**	**T**	**F**	**S**
	1	2	3	4	5	6
7	8	9	10	11	12	13
14	15	16	17	18	19	20
21	22	23	24	25	26	27
28						

1. The date is the fifteenth.

2. The date is a Wednesday.

3. It is after the twenty-fourth.

4. It is before the sixth.

5. It is an even-numbered date.

A die is rolled once. Find the probability rolling each of the following.

6. a 5

7. a 2

8. an odd number

9. a 5 or a 6

10. a number less than 3

11. *not* a 4

12. a number less than 1

13. *not* a 3 or a 4

14. a number less than 10

15. a 2, a 3, or a 4

Two dice are rolled once. The possible outcomes
are listed at the right. Find each probability.

6,1	6,2	6,3	6,4	6,5	6,6
5,1	5,2	5,3	5,4	5,5	5,6
4,1	4,2	4,3	4,4	4,5	4,6
3,1	3,2	3,3	3,4	3,5	3,6
2,1	2,2	2,3	2,4	2,5	2,6
1,1	1,2	1,3	1,4	1,5	1,6

16. P(5,5)

17. P(2,1)

18. P(an odd sum)

19. P(a sum of 7)

20. P(a sum of 11)

21. P(neither number 4)

22. P(a product less than 8)

23. P(neither number 3 or 4)

24. P(a sum of 4 or 10)

25. P(both numbers different)

Solve.

26. A dish of nuts has 12 walnuts, 8 pecans, and 4 cashews. Bhatti takes one without looking. What is the probability it is a pecan?

27. There are 15 girls and 11 boys in the class. One is chosen at random to attend a play. What is the probability that a girl is chosen?

PRACTICE WORKSHEET 9-3

Proportion

Determine if each pair of ratios forms a proportion.

1. 3 to 6, 4 to 5

2. 2 to 3, 1 to 2

3. 4 to 3, 3 to 4

4. 5:25, 2:10

5. 19:20, 38:40

6. 2:5, 11:25

7. 4 to 5, 24 to 25

8. 28:50, 43:53

9. 8 to 13, 32 to 52

10. 30 to 24, 48 to 40

11. 35:21, 5:3

12. 6:10 , 20:12

13. 3 to 6, 30 to 60

14. 5:4, 25:16

15. 36:18, 33:15

16. 9:2, 27:6

17. 400 to 4, 50 to 5

18. 9:15, 36:60

19. 100 to 20, 10 to 2

20. 2 to 7, 6 to 28

21. 125:75, 30:18

PRACTICE WORKSHEET 9-4

Solving Proportions

Solve each proportion.

1. $\frac{3}{4} = \frac{t}{12}$

2. $\frac{5}{g} = \frac{50}{80}$

3. $\frac{b}{8} = \frac{7}{10}$

4. $\frac{5}{9} = \frac{70}{r}$

5. $\frac{8}{11} = \frac{c}{44}$

6. $\frac{15}{17} = \frac{3}{h}$

7. $\frac{6}{18} = \frac{z}{9}$

8. $\frac{x}{35} = \frac{4}{7}$

9. $\frac{18}{p} = \frac{5}{11}$

10. $\frac{21}{24} = \frac{14}{e}$

11. $\frac{16}{d} = \frac{12}{9}$

12. $\frac{s}{14} = \frac{6}{70}$

13. $\frac{f}{18} = \frac{24}{9}$

14. $\frac{32}{48} = \frac{4}{z}$

15. $\frac{2}{21} = \frac{g}{84}$

16. $\frac{36}{y} = \frac{8}{12}$

17. $\frac{t}{4} = \frac{51}{18}$

18. $\frac{6}{7} = \frac{24}{c}$

19. $\frac{13}{52} = \frac{k}{8}$

20. $\frac{35}{w} = \frac{25}{5}$

21. $\frac{m}{90} = \frac{31}{9}$

PRACTICE WORKSHEET 9-5

Scale Drawings

Find the actual distances. Use the scale drawing of the tennis court at the right.

1. What is the length of the entire court?

2. What is the width of the court for singles?

3. What is the width of the court for doubles?

4. What is the distance from the service line to the net?

5. What is the height of the net?

6. What is the distance from the base line to the nearest service line?

Find the distance on a scale drawing for each actual distance. The scale is 1 in.:800 ft.

7. 1,200 ft

8. 3,200 ft

9. 600 ft

10. 300 ft

11. 50 ft

12. 450 ft

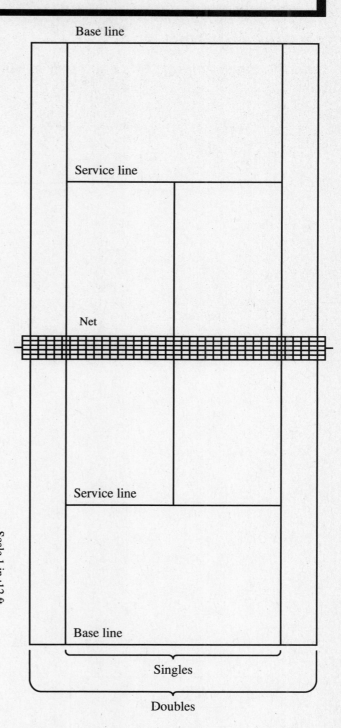

Base line

Service line

Net

Service line

Base line

Scale 1 in.:12 ft

Singles

Doubles

Solve. Use the scale 1 in.:8 ft.

13. If a classroom measures 20 feet by 32 feet, what are the dimensions of the room on the scale drawing?

14. The cafeteria of the school is shown on the drawing as being 10 inches by $12\frac{1}{2}$ inches. What are the actual dimensions of the cafeteria?

PRACTICE WORKSHEET 9-6

Similar Figures

Find the missing length for each pair of similar figures.

1.

2 cm ▭ 6 cm

s ▭ 12 m

2.

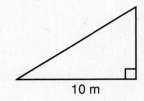

y   10 m

6 m   8 m

3.

7 in.   10 in.

k   500 in.

4.

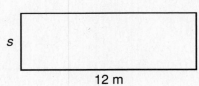

6 cm   5.5 cm

1.2 cm ▱ 1.1 cm   h

5.

7 mm   7 mm

56 mm   d

6.

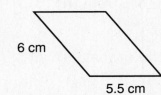

72 in.

48 in.   60 in.

s

7.

24 ft

16 ft

m   15 ft

8.

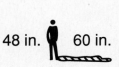

12 m   20 m

x   16 m

Name _____ **Date** _____

PRACTICE WORKSHEET 9-7

Applications: Planning a Trip

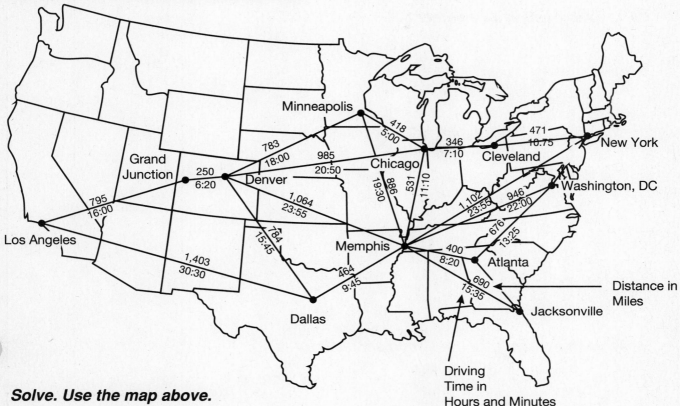

Solve. Use the map above.

1. What is the distance from Chicago to Denver?

2. What is the driving time from Los Angeles to Dallas?

3. What is the distance from New York to Chicago via Cleveland?

4. What is the driving time from Denver to Chicago via Memphis?

5. It took Mr. Chou 18 hours to drive from Denver to Minneapolis. What was his average speed?

6. How long would it take to travel from New York to Memphis if you could average 50 mph?

7. What is the shortest route shown from Minneapolis to Dallas?

8. It took the Sanchez family 34 hours to drive from Minneapolis to Dallas. What route did they most likely take?

PRACTICE WORKSHEET 9-8

Ratios, Percents, and Fractions

Write each fraction as a percent.

1. $\frac{31}{100}$

2. $\frac{3}{100}$

3. $\frac{2}{5}$

4. $\frac{7}{4}$

5. $\frac{3}{10}$

6. $\frac{6}{25}$

7. $\frac{7}{8}$

8. $\frac{9}{20}$

9. $\frac{4}{5}$

10. $\frac{17}{50}$

11. $\frac{3}{4}$

12. $\frac{19}{25}$

13. $1\frac{1}{4}$

14. $1\frac{1}{2}$

15. $\frac{5}{6}$

16. $\frac{9}{50}$

Write each percent as a fraction in simplest form.

17. 13%

18. 3%

19. 65%

20. 46%

21. 300%

22. 55%

23. 175%

24. 96%

25. 60%

26. 37.5%

27. 250%

28. $83\frac{1}{3}\%$

29. $33\frac{1}{3}\%$

30. 100%

31. 12%

32. 0.5%

Solve.

33. If $\frac{1}{8} = 12\frac{1}{2}\%$, what percent is equivalent to $\frac{5}{8}$?

34. On the average, 7 people out of 28 ride the bus to work. What percent do not ride the bus to work?

PRACTICE WORKSHEET 9-9

Percents and Decimals

Write each decimal as a percent.

1. 0.34

2. 0.715

3. 0.04

4. 1.52

5. 3.1

6. 0.605

7. 1.2

8. 0.6

9. 0.79

10. 0.004

11. 7.7

12. 0.09

13. 0.349

14. 0.1

15. 0.076

16. 5.525

Write each percent as a decimal.

17. 65%

18. 26.3%

19. 2%

20. 1.52%

21. $\frac{7}{10}$%

22. 450%

23. 0.9%

24. 90%

25. 300%

26. 0.2%

27. 79%

28. $34\frac{9}{10}$%

29. 7.7%

30. $7\frac{1}{2}$%

31. 175%

32. $4\frac{1}{4}$%

Solve.

33. In a group of 100 people, 52 have brown hair, 29 have blond hair, and 19 people have red hair. What percent of the people have either blond or red hair?

Glencoe Division, Macmillan/McGraw-Hill

PRACTICE WORKSHEET 9-10

Problem-Solving Strategy: Guess and Check

Solve. Use the guess-and-check strategy.

1. Mrs. Alvirez is three times as old as her daughter. In 12 years, she will be twice as old as her daughter. What are their ages now?

2. Notebook paper can be purchased in packages of 75 or 100 sheets of paper. Niki buys 6 packages and gets 475 sheets. How many packages of 100 sheets of paper does she buy?

3. Bus fare is 75¢. Rob needed change to ride the bus home from the shopping center. He reached in his pocket and pulled out 5 coins, none larger than a quarter, that totaled 75¢. What were the coins?

4. The Murphys spent exactly $13 on movie tickets. Adult tickets cost $3 each. Children's tickets cost $1.75 each. They bought more children's tickets. How many of each did they buy?

5. The difference between two whole numbers is 10. Their product is 375. Find the two numbers.

6. Brian is four times as old as his sister Jan. In six years, Brian will be twice as old as Jan. How old is Brian now?

7. Jack has 6 coins in his pocket. The coins are nickels, dimes, and quarters. The total value of the coins is 60¢. How many of each coin does Jack have?

8. The sum of four consecutive whole numbers is 54. Find the four numbers.

PRACTICE WORKSHEET 10-1

Finding the Percent of a Number

Find each percentage. Use a decimal for the percent.

1. 31% of 600

2. 9% of 70

3. 12% of 1,875

4. 38% of 4,250

5. 1% of 400

6. 15% of 72

7. 43% of 9,200

8. 3% of 150

9. 52% of 400

10. 4% of 20

Find each percentage. Use a fraction for the percent.

11. 50% of 30

12. 40% of 65

13. 20% of 70

14. 25% of 160

15. $66\frac{2}{3}$% of 360

16. 60% of 45

17. 75% of 64

18. 10% of 210

19. $33\frac{1}{3}$% of 99

20. 80% of 20

The Correa family's monthly take-home pay is $2,125. This table shows their monthly budget. Find how much the Correas spend on each expense.

Expense	Percent of take-home pay
Housing	31%
Food	37%
Clothing	15%
Entertainment	6%
Transportation	9%
Savings	2%

21. housing

22. food

23. clothing

24. entertainment

25. transportation

26. savings

PRACTICE WORKSHEET 10-2

Finding What Percent One Number Is of Another

Find each percent. Use an equation.

1. What percent of 50 is 7?

2. 16 is what percent of 30?

3. What percent of 80 is 120?

4. What percent of 40 is 90?

5. 6 is what percent of 24?

6. What percent of 15 is 5?

7. What percent of 20 is 29?

8. 15 is what percent of 60?

9. 63 is what percent of 42?

10. What percent of 72 is 9?

11. What percent of 80 is 4?

12. 6 is what percent of 1,200?

13. What percent of 60 is 12?

14. 8 is what percent of 32?

15. What percent of 20 is 25?

16. 2 is what percent of 1,000?

Solve.

17. A model rocket usually sells for $4.00. Jamie got an $0.80 discount. What percent of the original price is the discount?

18. Dinah bought a $50 coat for $27. What percent of the original price is the sale price?

19. Josephine put $75 down on the purchase of a $300 stereo system. She will pay the rest when it is delivered. What percent of the total price is her down payment?

20. David bought a backpack for $14. The sales tax on his purchase was $0.70. What percent of the purchase price is the sales tax?

PRACTICE WORKSHEET 10-3

Finding a Number When a Percent of It Is Known

Find each number. Use an equation.

1. 30% of what number is 120?

2. 25% of what number is 60?

3. 8 is 5% of what number?

4. 100 is 100% of what number?

5. 80% of what number is 40?

6. 12% of what number is 42?

7. 420 is 60% of what number?

8. 25% of what number is 62.5?

9. 25 is $62\frac{1}{2}$% of what number?

10. 40% of what number is 80?

11. 50% of what number is 350?

12. 200% of what number is 800?

13. 54 is 75% of what number?

14. 40% of what number is 400?

15. $33\frac{1}{3}$% of what number is 80?

16. 18 is $37\frac{1}{2}$% of what number?

17. 28% of what number is 7?

18. 90 is 150% of what number?

19. $87\frac{1}{2}$% of what number is 70?

20. 28 is 80% of what number?

Solve.

21. In a school survey, 60% of the students said they own calculators. 210 sudents said they own calculators. How many students were surveyed?

22. The Bulldogs have won 80% of their basketball games. If they lost 4 games, how many games have they played?

PRACTICE WORKSHEET 10-4

Problem-Solving Strategy: Using Venn Diagrams

Solve. Use a Venn diagram.

1. How many students take a non-English language class?

2. How many students take both Spanish and French?

3. How many students take both Spanish and German?

4. How many students take all three languages?

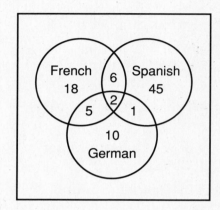

5. Suppose the school has 300 students. How many students do not take a language other than English?

6. Suppose the school has 300 students. What percent of students take a non-English language?

At Highwood High School, 36 freshmen are taking woodworking, 25 freshmen are taking cooking, and 9 freshmen are taking both courses. There are 100 students in the freshmen class.

Freshman Class

Solve.

7. Draw the Venn diagram.

8. How many freshmen are taking only cooking?

9. How many freshmen are taking only woodworking?

10. How many freshmen are taking neither woodworking nor cooking?

Solve. Use any strategy.

11. A pizza shop offers 6 toppings on its pizzas. How many combinations of 2 toppings are possible?

12. One number is $\frac{2}{3}$ of another. Their sum is 60. What are the two numbers?

PRACTICE WORKSHEET 10-5

Estimating the Percent of a Number

Estimate.

1. 21% of 38   **2.** 38% of 120   **3.** 27% of 82

4. 32% of 110   **5.** 146% of 52   **6.** 42% of 91

7. 79% of 203   **8.** 53% of 300   **9.** 91% of 500

10. 64% of 178   **11.** 0.5% of 600   **12.** 18% of 44

13. 41% of 60   **14.** 34% of 16   **15.** 24% of 64

16. 17% of 36   **17.** 86% of 25   **18.** 11% of 207

19. 27% of 46   **20.** 33% of 125   **21.** 48% of 76

22. 68% of 66   **23.** 39% of 52   **24.** 89% of 298

25. 63% of 40   **26.** 173% of 84   **27.** 85% of 72

Solve.

28. 24% of the cars in the parking lot were blue. If there were 87 cars in the lot, about how many of them were blue?

29. Sharon got 85% of the test questions done correctly. If there were 40 test questions, how many did Sharon get right?

PRACTICE WORKSHEET 10-6

Percent of Change

Find the percent of increase. Round to the nearest percent.

1. original weight, 120 lb
   new weight, 125 lb

2. original volume, 3 L
   new volume, 3.09 L

3. original price, $12
   new price, $13.50

4. original number, 520
   new number, 640

5. original weight, 3.2 oz
   new weight, 4.2 oz

6. original price, $2.99
   new price, $3.29

Find the percent of decrease. Round to the nearest percent.

7. original price, $15
   new price, $11

8. original price, $500
   new price, $450

9. original weight, 85 lb
   new weight, 78 lb

10. original number, 650
    new number, 575

11. original price, $9.95
    new price, $6.75

12. original weight, 8 kg
    new weight, 7.5 kg

Solve. Round to the nearest percent.

13. A vitamin used to be packaged in bottles of 60. Now there are 75 vitamins per bottle. What is the percent of increase?

14. Larry and Sue used to have 65 customers on their paper route. Now they have 59. What is the percent of decrease?

15. A pair of shoes was $50 one year and $52.50 the next year. What is the percent of increase?

16. Groceries cost $60 but, after redeeming coupons, the bill was $55.70. What is the percent of decrease?

Name _____ **Date** _____

PRACTICE WORKSHEET 10-7

Discount

Find the discount and the sale price.

1. television, $500
   discount rate, 15%

2. bicycle, $149.50
   discount rate, 20%

3. typewriter, $240
   discount rate, 10%

4. watch, $35.75
   discount rate, 15%

Find the discount and the discount rate.
Round the discount rate to the nearest percent.

5. violin, $160
   sale price, $140

6. golf clubs, $125
   sale price, $99.95

7. fishing rod, $35
   sale price, $28.50

8. computer, $795
   sale price, $725

9. roller skates, $179
   sale price, $150

10. video cassette, $20
    sale price, $13.50

11. encyclopedia, $699
    sale price, $599

12. cordless phone, $125
    sale price, $89.99

Glencoe Division, Macmillan/McGraw-Hill

PRACTICE WORKSHEET 10-8

Interest

Find the interest owed on each loan. Then find the total amount to be repaid.

1. principal: $300
   annual rate: 12%
   time: 2 years

2. principal: $750
   annual rate: 8%
   time: 6 months

3. principal: $4,000
   annual rate: $10\frac{1}{2}$%
   time: 4 years

4. principal: $980
   annual rate: 11%
   time: 24 months

5. principal: $30,000
   annual rate: $12\frac{1}{2}$%
   time: 25 years

6. principal: $1,250
   rate: $1\frac{1}{2}$% per month
   time: 2 months

Find the interest earned on each deposit.

7. principal: $3,340
   annual rate: $5\frac{1}{2}$%
   time: 8 months

8. principal: $875
   annual rate: 6%
   time: 4 years

9. principal: $1,350
   annual rate: $6\frac{1}{4}$%
   time: 6 months

10. principal: $7,200
    annual rate: $9\frac{1}{2}$%
    time: $1\frac{1}{4}$ years

11. principal: $5,000
    annual rate: $7\frac{1}{4}$ %
    time: 3 years

12. principal: $8,900
    annual rate: $10\frac{1}{2}$%
    time: 18 months

Solve.

13. Chin borrowed $1,500 from the bank at $9\frac{1}{2}$% interest per year for 6 months. How much did he have to pay back at the end of the 6-month period?

14. Sarah lent Nathan $450 at 6% annual interest to be paid back in 4 months. How much should Sarah receive when Nathan repays the loan?

PRACTICE WORKSHEET 10-9

Applications: Compound Interest

Find the savings total for each account.

1. principal: $400
   annual rate: 6%
   compounded quarterly
   time: 1 year

2. principal: $600
   annual rate: 5%
   compounded quarterly
   time: 6 months

3. principal: $750
   annual rate: 7%
   compounded semiannually
   time: 1 year

4. principal: $2,000
   annual rate: 8%
   compounded semiannually
   time: 2 years

Solve.

5. Daniel is planning to deposit $500 in one of two savings accounts.
   One account pays 6% simple interest. The other pays $5\frac{1}{2}$% interest compounded
   quarterly. In which account would he have the greater total at the end of
   1 year? How much greater?

6. Rita has $500 to deposit. The Sun Bank pays 6% interest compounded quarterly.
   The Star Bank pays 6% interest compounded semiannually. The Moon Bank pays
   6% compounded annually. Which bank pays the most interest?

7. How much interest does each bank pay? What is the difference between the
   interest paid by the highest and lowest paying banks?

PRACTICE WORKSHEET 10-10

Problem Solving: Using Percent

Solve.

1. Martin saves $63 each week. If he saves 15% of his wages, how much does he earn per week?

2. Stuart wants to gain 15 pounds. This is 12% of his present weight. How much does Stuart weigh now?

3. During a sale, Ms. Trevino puchased a blender for 75% of the regular price. She paid $27 for the blender. What was the regular price?

4. When a truck is loaded to 45% of its capacity, there are 108 cases on the truck. How many cases will be on the truck when it is loaded to capacity?

5. Betty bought a camera at a 20% reduction sale. If she paid $18 for it, what was the regular price?

6. If 48% of the students in a school are boys, and the girls number 468, how many students are enrolled?

7. If an ore contains 16% copper, how many tons of ore are needed to get 20 tons of copper?

8. Patricia Walsh receives a base salary of $125 plus a commission of 6% of sales. If her pay for one week was $441.80, what were her total sales?

9. Christopher Cernami answered 4 test questions incorrectly and scored 90%. How many questions did he answer correctly?

10. The Sluggerville baseball team won 32 games. Their percent of games lost was 20%. Find the number of games the team played.

PRACTICE WORKSHEET 11-1

Median, Mode, and Range

Find the median, mode, and range for each set of data.

1. 51, 47, 48, 51, 49, 51, 52

2. 114, 117, 114, 119, 115, 116, 112

3. 10, 15, 10, 15, 4, 1, 4, 15, 10, 15, 11, 11, 7

4. 49, 52, 54, 51, 60, 57, 73, 51, 55, 57, 53, 57

5. 172, 176, 172, 177, 177, 175, 175, 178, 172, 174, 177

6. 9.2, 8.6, 9.3, 9.7, 7.2, 9.6, 9.9, 9.5, 9.4

7. 0.64, 1.62, 1.66, 0.62, 1.66, 0.64, 0.62, 1.62

8. 160, 156, 160, 315, 159, 160, 153, 251, 158, 150

Solve.

9. Allan scored 87, 92, 85, 88, and 84 on math tests this semester. What is the median of these scores? The range?

10. On his next test, Allan scored 98. How does this affect the median? How does it affect the range?

PRACTICE WORKSHEET 11-2

Frequency Tables

1. Complete the frequency column of this table.

Score	Tally	Frequency
1	TＨＬ IIII	
2	TＨＬ TＨＬ IIII	
3	TＨＬ III	
4	TＨＬ TＨＬ TＨＬ TＨＬ II	
5	TＨＬ I	
6	TＨＬ TＨＬ TＨＬ III	

Find each of the following.
Round to the nearest tenth.

2. mean

3. median

4. mode

5. range

Solve. Use the data at the right. Round to the nearest tenth.

6. Make a frequency table for this set of data.

Number of Children in each family
2 2 5 2 2
5 3 1 3 1
4 2 1 5 2
2 1 3 4 2

7. Find the mean.

8. Find the median.

9. Find the mode.

10. Find the range.

11. Make a frequency table for this set of data.

12. Find the mean.

13. Find the median.

14. Find the mode.

15. Find the range.

Hours Practiced Each Week by Band Members
4 3 7 7 4
4 7 4 9 3
3 5 9 9 9
4 4 5 3 7
7 7 5 4 4

PRACTICE WORKSHEET 11-3

Applications: Misusing Statistics

The commissions earned last month by salespeople at Electronics City are shown at the right.

Commission	Number of Salespeople
$ 500	7
$ 800	5
$1,000	3
$2,200	1
$2,800	2
$5,400	2

1. Find the mean, median, and mode of the commission amounts earned.

2. Which "average" would you use in an advertisement to hire new salespeople? Why?

3. Which "average" best describes the commission earned by all salespeople? Why?

The number of yards a football player gained by rushing during each game of a season are shown at the right.

38	42	54	47
46	62	64	58

4. Find the mean and median of the yards rushed per game to the nearest tenth.

5. Which "average" best describes the yards rushed per game? Why?

6. Instead of rushing for 38 yards in one game, suppose the player rushed for 102 yards. How would the mean and median be affected?

7. Now which "average" best describes the yards rushed per game? Why?

The prices of different camcorders carried by a store are listed at the right.

$ 899
$ 999
$ 950
$ 1,950
$ 1,099

8. Find the mean and median prices.

9. Which "average" best describes the price of a camcorder? Why?

10. Suppose that the store replaces the most expensive camcorder with a model priced at $1,100. How would the mean and median be affected?

PRACTICE WORKSHEET 11-4

Bar Graphs

Make a vertical bar graph for each set of data.

1.

Average Points Scored per Basketball Game	
Wildcats	62
Rockets	74
Panthers	85
Bulldogs	78
Jets	87
Cougars	66

2.

1988 Population	
Chicago	3,000,000
Houston	1,700,000
Los Angeles	3,400,000
New York	7,400,000
Philadelphia	1,600,000

Make a horizontal bar graph for each set of data.

3.

Annual Rainfall (in inches)	
1987	45
1988	32
1989	27
1990	35
1991	48

4.

Average Miles per Gallon of Gas	
Car A	32
Car B	26
Car C	22
Car D	28
Car E	31
Car F	24

Glencoe Division, Macmillan/McGraw-Hill

PRACTICE WORKSHEET 11-5

Line Graphs

Make a line graph for each set of data.

1.

Price per Gallon of Regular Gasoline	
1965	$0.31
1970	$0.36
1975	$0.58
1980	$1.19
1985	$1.12

2.

Minimum Hourly Wage Rate	
1950	$0.75
1960	$1.00
1970	$1.60
1980	$3.10
1990	$3.35

3.

Motor Vehicle Registrations	
1935	26.2 million
1945	31.0 million
1955	62.7 million
1965	90.4 million
1975	132.9 million
1985	171.7 million

4.

Average Speed of Indianapolis 500 Winners (in mph)	
1960	139
1965	151
1970	156
1975	159
1980	143
1985	153
1990	186

Name _____   Date _____

Pictographs

Make a pictograph for each set of data.

1.

TVs Sold	
January	20
February	18
March	5
April	24
May	12
June	9

2.

Pennant Sales	
Sunday	50
Monday	35
Tuesday	25
Wednesday	20
Thursday	40

3.

Movie Attendance	
Sunday	140
Monday	90
Tuesday	100
Wednesday	120
Thursday	150
Friday	170
Saturday	160

4.

Music Store Sales	
Rock	8,500
Classical	4,250
Country	4,000
Other	3,750

Glencoe Division, Macmillan/McGraw-Hill

PRACTICE WORKSHEET 11-7

Circle Graphs

Make a circle graph for each set of data.

1.

Redalgo Family Budget	
Food	25%
Housing	30%
Clothing	15%
Transportation	15%
Recreation	10%
Other	5%

2.

Materials Used to Generate Power in the U.S.	
Oil	50%
Gas	25%
Coal	15%
Nuclear	5%
Water	5%

3.

Attendance at Concert	
Children	10%
Teens	40%
Adults	35%
Senior Citizens	15%

4.

Sales of Electronics	
TVs	30%
VCRs	20%
Stereo equipment	25%
Personal computers	10%
Video games	10%
Other	5%

Glencoe Division, Macmillan/McGraw-Hill

PRACTICE WORKSHEET 11-8

Stem-and-Leaf Plots

State the stems that you would use to plot each set of data.

1. 72, 85, 53, 57, 74, 79

2. 26, 3, 38, 15, 29, 36

3. 1.4, 2.8, 1.9, 3.7, 2.6, 4.5

4. 536, 738, 104, 427, 326, 258

Find the median and mode of the data in each stem-and-leaf plot.

5.

Stem	Leaf
4	1 2 5
5	3 5 7
6	4 5 6 8

6.

Stem	Leaf
2	3 5 9
3	4 6 8 9
4	2 3 3 7

7.

Stem	Leaf
0	3 7 7 8
1	2 4 8 9
2	0 1 1 3
3	2 5 8

Use the ages at the right to complete problems 8–11.

15	6	19	24	37	58	24
8	27	39	18	54	25	32
50	35	31	53	9	28	

8. Construct a stem-and-leaf plot of the data.

9. What is the youngest age?

10. What is the range of the ages?

11. How many ages are above 20?

12. Use the data at the right to construct a stem-and-leaf plot. In which interval were the most jeans priced?

Prices of Different Style Jeans (in dollars)							
24	19	36	29	42	37	32	27
25	60	32	62	45	29	37	42
19	44	36	28	40	37	31	58

Glencoe Division, Macmillan/McGraw-Hill

PRACTICE WORKSHEET 11-9

Measures of Variation

Find the upper quartile, lower quartile, and interquartile range for each set of data.

1. 2, 5, 7, 9, 10, 12, 14, 18

2. 17, 18, 54, 57, 60, 62, 74, 76, 80, 81

3. 39, 48, 57, 24, 35, 32, 42, 56

4. 64, 27, 39, 56, 57, 16, 60, 72, 38, 41

5.

Stem	Leaf
2	4 5
3	0 1 2
4	5 8
5	2 4 9

6.

Stem	Leaf
0	4
1	1 1 5 6 8
2	3 4
3	2 7

7.

Stem	Leaf
5	0 0 1 3
6	5 8 8
7	1 2 4
8	7 9

8.

Stem	Leaf
8	2 4
9	3 5 6 8 9
10	2 4 7 8
11	2

2 | 4 represents 24.   3 | 2 represents 32.   5 | 0 represents 50.   11 | 2 represents 112.

Solve. Use the data at the right.

9. Make a stem-and-leaf plot for each store's data.

Customers per Hour		
Time	**Rags & Riches**	**Jean Joint**
10:00–10:59	24	15
11:00–11:59	36	32
12:00–12:59	54	57
1:00– 1:59	42	38
2:00– 2:59	38	29
3:00– 3:59	14	28
4:00– 4:59	52	35
5:00– 5:59	49	39
6:00– 6:59	22	40
7:00– 7:59	48	32
8:00– 8:59	25	37
9:00– 9:59	16	24

10. Find the interquartile range of each store's data.

11. From your findings in Problem 10, which store has the more consistent number of customers per hour?

PRACTICE WORKSHEET 11-10

Box-and-Whisker Plots

The number of hours worked in one month by part-time salespeople at Discount Mart is displayed at the right. Use this box-and-whisker plot to answer each question.

10   20   30   40   50   60   70

1. Which of these pieces of information can be found on this box-and-whisker plot: mean, median, mode, range?

2. What is the range of the data?

3. What part of the data is greater than 50?

4. The middle half of the data is between what two numbers?

5. State the median, upper and lower quartiles, and the interquartile range of the data.

The fuel efficiency of twelve different cars was tested, and the data are shown at the right. Use these data for Problems 6–9.

Miles per Gallon of Gas
19 21 20 38 42 28
24 37 33 18 26 20

6. Construct a box-and-whisker plot of the data.

7. Find the mean, median, mode, and range of the data. Which of these pieces of information could you find from the box-and-whisker plot?

8. What part of the data is greater than 25?

9. State the upper and lower quartiles and the interquartile range of the data.

PRACTICE WORKSHEET 11-11

Problem-Solving Strategy: Look for a Pattern

Solve.

1. Rhonda swam 4 laps the first day, 6 laps the second day, 8 laps the third day, and so on until she could swim 20 laps. How many days did it take her to reach 20 laps?

2. A dropped ball from a high place falls 32 ft the first second, 32 ft × 4 the second second, and 32 ft × 9 the third second. How far does it fall the fifth second?

3. From one corner of a four-sided figure, one diagonal can be drawn. From one corner of a five-sided figure, two diagonals can be drawn. How many diagonals can be drawn from one corner of a nine-sided figure?

4. Tina started working at an hourly wage of $4.40. She will get a 20¢ raise every 6 months. What will be her hourly rate after working 3 years?

5. Each of the 8 people at the party exchanges greetings with each other person at the party. How many exchanges of greeting are there?

6. A new music store had 20 customers the first day it was open. The number of customers doubled each day for the next four days. How many customers did the store have on the fifth day?

7. Sixteen teams are involved in a single-elimination tournament. When a team loses, it is eliminated. How many games are needed to determine this tournament's winner?

8. Danny plans to do 5 more push-ups each day until he can do 75. He begins with 15. How many days will it take him?

PRACTICE WORKSHEET 12-1

Integers

Replace ◯ with <, >, or = to make a true sentence.

1. −12 ◯ 15

2. 6 ◯ 18

3. 13 ◯ −21

4. 9 ◯ 6

5. −2.3 ◯ −2.2

6. −4 ◯ −12

7. −7 ◯ 7

8. −7 ◯ 5

9. 9 ◯ −2

10. |18| ◯ |−14|

11. |−13| ◯ |−15|

12. |−12| ◯ |12|

13. |−3| ◯ |7|

14. |0| ◯ |−5|

15. |−10| ◯ |4|

16. |8| ◯ |−8|

17. |−13| ◯ |−6|

18. |4| ◯ |−11|

Order from least to greatest.

19. 5, 8, −2, 0, −4

20. −1, 6, 2, 5, −3

21. 1, 0, −1, −8, −7, −3

22. 1, −6, 4, −4, 7, −1

23. 0, −7, 2, −9, 5, 3

24. 1, 4, −2, 8, −5, −9

25. 4, −3, 7, 1, 0, −2

26. 5, −2, −5, 0, 2, 1

27. −7, 2, −1, −9, 3

28. 1, −3, −5, 4, −2, 6

Complete.

29. If −6 indicates a drop of 6°C in temperature, what does 6 indicate?

30. If 31 indicates 31 seconds after a rocket launch, what does −31 indicate?

PRACTICE WORKSHEET 12-2

Adding Integers

Write an equation for each number line. Then solve.

1.

2.

3.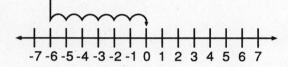

4.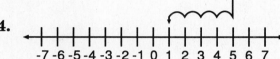

Add. Use a number line if necessary.

5. $21 + (-8)$ **6.** $-6 + 4$ **7.** $13 + (-19)$

8. $-2 + 6$ **9.** $41 + 3$ **10.** $-7 + (-5)$

11. $-12 + (-15)$ **12.** $3 + (-3)$ **13.** $-1.1 + (-2)$

14. $4.3 + 1.3$ **15.** $-5.2 + 3.4$ **16.** $9 + (-7)$

17. $-7 + 11$ **18.** $-4.2 + (-8.5)$ **19.** $3 + 5$

20. $-3 + 15$ **21.** $\frac{4}{5} + \left(-\frac{3}{10}\right)$ **22.** $1 + (-7)$

23. $-\frac{1}{2} + \left(-\frac{3}{4}\right)$ **24.** $-\frac{2}{3} + \frac{5}{12}$ **25.** $6 + (-8)$

Solve.

26. The balance in Sally's checking account was $273.25. She wrote a check for $72.15 and made a deposit of $55.20. What is her new balance?

27. The plane was flying at 7,800 feet when it had to climb 2,500 feet to clear a mountain range. What was its new altitude?

28. Mark had business on the twenty-seventh floor. Later he went up 6 floors to the rooftop observatory. On what floor is the observatory?

29. Starting on their own 25-yard line, the Packers gain 8 yards, lose 5 yards, and gain 7 yards. What yard line are they on now?

PRACTICE WORKSHEET 12-3

Subtracting Integers

Subtract.

1. $9 - (-2)$

2. $-12 - (-5)$

3. $-3 - 16$

4. $2 - (-8)$

5. $15 - 6$

6. $-14 - 3$

7. $-11 - (-7)$

8. $1 - 13$

9. $9 - 2$

10. $-25 - (-16)$

11. $32 - (-7)$

12. $-3 - 21$

13. $72 - (-8)$

14. $61 - (-55)$

15. $1.9 - (-2.1)$

16. $-3 - (-5)$

17. $-1 - 4$

18. $-1.6 - 1.6$

19. $2 - 8$

20. $0.3 - (-1.9)$

21. $4 - (-1)$

22. $5 - (-5)$

23. $\frac{1}{6} - \frac{3}{4}$

24. $-\frac{5}{6} - \frac{1}{3}$

25. $\frac{7}{8} - \left(-\frac{1}{4}\right)$

26. $-10 - 5$

Solve.

27. Rocky's Flower Shop deposited checks and cash in the amount of $2,452.60 on Friday. On Monday the bank called to say that one of the checks had been returned. If that check was for $45.87, what was the actual deposit on Friday?

28. When Lucy received her checking account statement, it showed a balance of $515.63. Lucy's check register showed a deposit of $253.62 and two checks for $21.75 and $37.89 which were not included in the statement. What is Lucy's actual account balance?

29. Bob wrote a check for $15.75 to pay for a ticket to the symphony. The check was returned because the tickets had all been sold. Bob's check register showed a balance of $372.15. What is his new balance?

30. Jenny's balance was $349.95. She deposited three checks, $45.00, $125.63, and $38.25. She also withdrew $50.00 in cash. What is her new balance after these transactions?

PRACTICE WORKSHEET 12-4

Applications: *Windchill Factor*

Windchill Chart

Wind speed in mph	Actual temperature (°Fahrenheit)								
	50	40	30	20	10	0	-10	-20	-30
	Equivalent temperature (°Fahrenheit)								
0	50	40	30	20	10	0	-10	-20	-30
5	48	37	27	16	6	-5	-15	-26	-36
10	40	28	16	4	-9	-21	-33	-46	-58
15	36	22	9	-5	-18	-36	-45	-58	-72
20	32	18	4	-10	-25	-39	-53	-67	-82
25	30	16	0	-15	-29	-44	-59	-74	-88
30	28	13	-2	-18	-33	-48	-63	-79	-94

Use the chart above to find each equivalent temperature.

1. 40°F, 5 mph

2. −10°F, 20 mph

3. 0°F, 15 mph

4. 50°F, 10 mph

5. −20°F, 30 mph

6. 20°F, 10 mph

7. 40°F, 25 mph

8. 30°F, 0 mph

9. 10°F, 5 mph

10. −20°F, 15 mph

11. 0°F, 30 mph

12. −30°F, 0 mph

What is the difference between each actual temperature and the equivalent temperature when the wind speed is 10 mph?

13. 40°F

14. −20°F

15. 0°F

16. −30°F

17. 10°F

18. 20°F

Solve.

19. The actual temperature is −20°F. The equivalent temperature with the windchill factor is −74°F. What is the wind speed?

20. The wind speed is 15 mph. The equivalent temperature with the windchill factor is 9°F. What is the actual temperature?

PRACTICE WORKSHEET 12-5

Multiplying Integers

Multiply.

1. $9 \times (-2)$

2. $-12 \times (-5)$

3. -3×16

4. $2 \times (-8)$

5. 15×6

6. -14×3

7. $-11 \times (-7)$

8. 1×13

9. 9×15

10. $-25 \times (-16)$

11. $30 \times (-7)$

12. -3×21

13. $70 \times (-80)$

14. $61 \times (-59)$

15. $9.1 \times (-1.9)$

16. $-3.8 \times (-5.2)$

17. -6×0

18. -1.5×1.5

19. -7×8

20. $7 \times (-21)$

21. $0 \times (-2)$

22. $-\frac{2}{3} \times \left(-\frac{3}{4}\right)$

23. $-\frac{3}{4} \times \frac{1}{6}$

24. $6 \times (-10)$

25. $\frac{8}{9} \times \left(-\frac{1}{4}\right)$

26. $-4 \times (-25)$

Solve.

27. A deep-sea exploring ship is pulling up a diver at the rate of 25 feet per minute. The diver is 200 feet below sea level. How deep was the diver 10 minutes ago?

28. Joe is playing a game with a regular die. If the number that turns up is even, he will gain 5 times the number that comes up. If it is odd, he will lose 10 times the number that comes up. He tosses a 3. Express the result as an integer.

29. Barb's Swimsuit Outlet sold 312 swimsuits during a special sale where every suit was marked down to $9.99. Twenty-nine suits were returned for refunds. What was the actual income from the sale?

30. After a concert was canceled, ticket holders could exchange tickets for a future date or get a refund of the $20 price. Seven hundred tickets were returned for refunds. Express this income as an integer.

Glencoe Division, Macmillan/McGraw-Hill

PRACTICE WORKSHEET 12-6

Dividing Integers

Divide.

1. $18 \div (-3)$ 2. $-48 \div (-12)$

3. $-45 \div 15$ 4. $40 \div (-8)$

5. $0 \div 0$ 6. $-63 \div 3$

7. $-140 \div (-7)$ 8. $52 \div 13$

9. $-40 \div (-5)$ 10. $-120 \div (-6)$

11. $168 \div (-7)$ 12. $-210 \div 21$

13. $5,680 \div (-80)$ 14. $27 \div (-9)$

15. $0 \div (-1)$ 16. $-7.2 \div (-0.9)$

17. $-14.64 \div 4$ 18. $-15 \div 1.5$

19. $14 \div (-10)$ 20. $-25 \div (5)$

21. $4.4 \div (-2.2)$ 22. $-\frac{2}{3} \div \left(-\frac{4}{9}\right)$

23. $-\frac{3}{4} \div \frac{1}{8}$ 24. $-80 \div (-4)$

25. $\frac{8}{9} \div \left(-\frac{4}{15}\right)$ 26. $-4 \div 8$

27. $-18 \div 6$ 28. $51 \div (-3)$

29. $-91 \div (-13)$ 30. $-42 \div 14$

31. $-96 \div (-24)$ 32. $90 \div (-15)$

Solve.

33. Stan weighed 225 pounds on March 1. Four months later he weighed 197 pounds. What was his average change in weight per month?

34. In 1980, the population of Clayborn was 15,792. In 1986 the population was 19,296. What was the average change in population per year?

PRACTICE WORKSHEET 12-7

Problem-Solving Strategy: Work Backwards

Solve. Work backwards.

1. Eight times a number plus 7 is equal to 79. Find the number.

2. Twice a number decreased by 12 is equal to 10. Find the number.

3. Seven more than 3 times a number is equal to 49. Find the number.

4. If 8 is added to a number and then the number is divided by 3, the result is 12. Find the number.

5. Nine less than 6 times a number is equal to 93. Find the number.

6. If the sum of a number and 10 is divided by 3, the result is 13. Find the number.

7. If a number is multiplied by 4, then 6 is added to it, and the result is divided by 7, the answer is 6. Find the number.

8. If a number is divided by 8 and then 12 is added to the quotient, the result is 17. Find the number.

PRACTICE WORKSHEET 13-1

Solving Equations Using Addition or Subtraction

Solve each equation. Check your solution.

1. $13 = 9 + a$ **2.** $15 + b = -38$ **3.** $72 = a - 7$ **4.** $b - 15 = -38$

5. $t + (-27) = -10$ **6.** $4 + c = 9$ **7.** $c - (-8) = -17$ **8.** $-26 + r = 215$

9. $d - 4 = 9$ **10.** $e - 117 = -215$ **11.** $28 + x = 9$ **12.** $f - 57 = -121$

13. $8 = s + 1\frac{3}{5}$ **14.** $k + (-0.7) = -1.1$ **15.** $4 = g - 3\frac{3}{5}$ **16.** $h - 35 = 27$

17. $-13.2 + y = 10$ **18.** $n - 2.7 = 2.7$ **19.** $p - (-0.3) = -0.8$ **20.** $g + 0.3 = 0.8$

21. $q - 6.6 = -1.4$ **22.** $t + 86 = -14$ **23.** $v + (-1.7) = 3.2$ **24.** $r - 7.1 = 3.2$

Solve.

25. The high temperature today after a morning low of –10°F, is 25°F. How many degrees did the temperature rise?

26. There were 27 students in the library. Four left and then another group came in, bringing the total to 45. How many were in that group?

27. Bob is on a weight-loss program. He has lost 15.2 pounds so far. If he now weighs 197 pounds, how much did he weigh when he began?

28. Jane has $382.57 in her checking account. After writing a check for $451.25, what is her balance?

PRACTICE WORKSHEET 13-2

Solving Equations Using Multiplication or Division

Solve each equation. Check your solution.

1. $9 = \frac{a}{3}$

2. $84 = 7a$

3. $15b = -60$

4. $25 = \frac{b}{10}$

5. $c \div (-5) = 9$

6. $-4d = 0$

7. $\frac{d}{6} = -15$

8. $-4 = \frac{e}{-12}$

9. $-11e = -77$

10. $10 = g \div 7$

11. $6 = \frac{3}{4}g$

12. $-\frac{2}{3}j = 22$

13. $h \div 8 = 25$

14. $39 = -13k$

15. $75 = 25l$

16. $-7 = \frac{j}{2}$

17. $-56 = \frac{k}{-10}$

18. $-24 = 2m$

19. $\frac{m}{-5} = 2.25$

20. $27n = 27$

21. $3p = -45$

22. $12 = \frac{p}{-6}$

23. $11 = \frac{q}{9}$

24. $-6q = 3.6$

Solve.

25. The product of two numbers is 12. Their sum is –7. What are the numbers?

26. The quotient of two numbers is –1. Their difference is 8. What are the numbers?

27. When the cold front moved through, the temperature fell 24°F in 4 hours. What was the average temperature rise or fall per hour?

28. Brandon, Maria, Tonya, and Conrad shared the cost of a $12.76 pizza equally. What was each person's share?

PRACTICE WORKSHEET 13-3

Solving Two-Step Equations

Solve each equation. Check your solution.

1. $\frac{d}{6} + 7 = 18$ **2.** $2a + 7 = -3$ **3.** $3(p - 5) = 75$ **4.** $5t + (-32) = 43$

5. $2 + 5c = 17$ **6.** $\frac{j}{3} + 4 = -2$ **7.** $\frac{b}{-5} - 9 = 16$ **8.** $-2(2 + y) = 6$

9. $-42 = \frac{a}{3} - 9$ **10.** $25 = -3b - 2$ **11.** $\frac{c - 20}{-5} = -2$ **12.** $-18 = 5g + (-3)$

13. $-81 = 5e - 6$ **14.** $5 = \frac{f}{-4} - 3$ **15.** $3(d - 3) = -15$ **16.** $42 = -5k + 2$

17. $-11 = \frac{j}{3} - 2$ **18.** $\frac{2}{7}(h + 5) = 4$ **19.** $25 = \frac{l}{3} + 26$ **20.** $-2 + 6m = 22$

Solve.

21. Four times a number is added to 12. The result is –28. What is the number?

22. Half of a number is subtracted from 19. The result is 13. What is the number?

23. If Marilyn buys 3 more compact discs, she will have twice as many discs as Sharon. Sharon has 12 discs. How many discs does Marilyn have?

24. Milton is $30 short of having half the money he needs to buy a $400 bicycle. How much money does Milton have?

Glencoe Division, Macmillan/McGraw-Hill

PRACTICE WORKSHEET 13-4

The Coordinate Plane

Find the ordered pair for each point labeled on the coordinate plane.

1. *A*   2. *B*

3. *C*   4. *D*

5. *E*   6. *F*

7. *G*   8. *H*

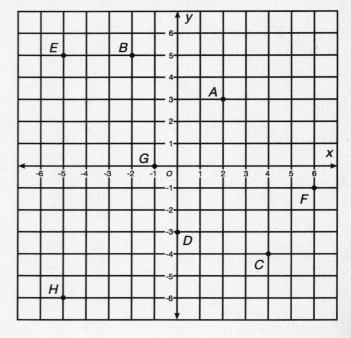

Draw coordinate axes on the grid at the right. Graph each ordered pair. Label each point with the given letter.

9. *A* (3, 4)   10. *B* (–2, 1)

11. *C* (–5, –5)   12. *D* (2, –1)

13. *E* (2, 3)   14. *F* (–2, 5)

15. *G* (–1, 0)   16. *H* (0, –1)

17. *J* (–2, –3)   18. *K* (2, 5)

19. *L* (–5, 2)   20. *M* (5, 5)

21. *N* (1, 2)   22. *P* (–1, –1)

23. *Q* (4, 5)   24. *R* (5, –4)

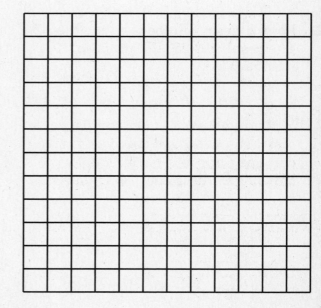

Glencoe Division, Macmillan/McGraw-Hill

PRACTICE WORKSHEET 13-5

Graphing Equations

Graph the solutions to each equation.

1. $3x = y$

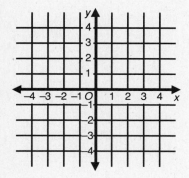

2. $-4x = y$

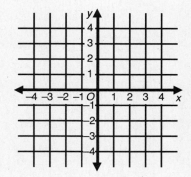

3. $y = x + 3$

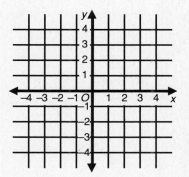

4. $x - 2 = y$

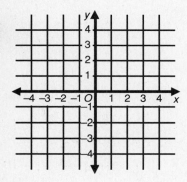

5. $\frac{2}{5}x = y$

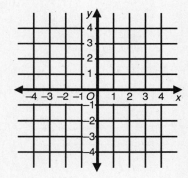

6. $x + y = 1$

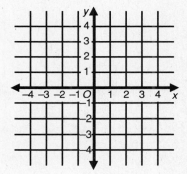

7. $x - y = 3$

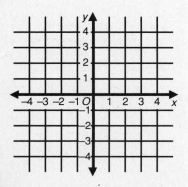

8. $y = \frac{x}{4}$

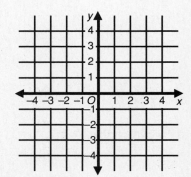

9. $x + y = 0$

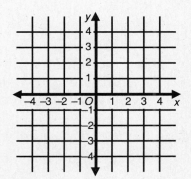

PRACTICE WORKSHEET 13-6

Applications: Reading a Grid Map

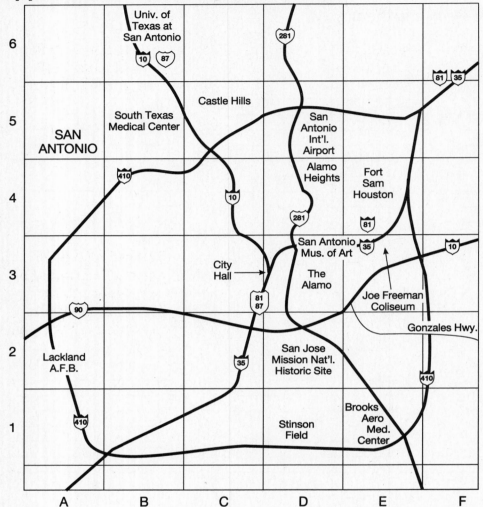

Use the map above.

1. What hospital is located in B-5?

2. What airport is located in D-1?

3. What highway is the University of Texas at San Antonio near?

4. What highway passes through Lackland Air Force Base?

5. Which highways would you travel to go from City Hall to San Antonio International Airport?

Give the location of each as a letter-number pair.

6. Joe Freeman Coliseum

7. Castle Hills

8. San Antonio Museum of Art

9. Alamo Heights

10. San Jose Mission National Historic Site

11. Gonzales Highway

PRACTICE WORKSHEET 13-7

Problem-Solving Strategy: Writing an Equation

Solve. Write an equation.

1. Sheila has 5 fewer tapes than Cheryl. Together they have 33 tapes. How many tapes does each girl have?

2. Ted's highest bowling scores is 236. This is 10 less than three times his lowest score. What is Ted's lowest score?

3. Movie attendance at the 7:00 show was 342. This is 25 more than half the number of people who attended the 9:00 show. How many attended the 9:00 show?

4. Jody jogged and cycled a total of 130 miles last week. The number of miles she jogged is 2 more than one-third the number of miles she cycled. How many miles did she jog? Cycle?

5. A bookstore displayed 110 copies of the #1 bestseller in 12 rows. Five rows contained 2 fewer books than the other rows. How many books were in each row?

6. Marla earned $39 baby-sitting this week. On Saturday she baby-sat 1 hour more than twice the number of hours she baby-sat on Friday. If she earns $3 per hour, how many hours did she baby-sit each day?

PRACTICE WORKSHEET 14-1

Finding the Number of Outcomes

Use multiplication to find the number of possible outcomes. Draw a tree diagram to show the possible outcomes.

1. tossing a nickel, a dime, and a quarter

2. a choice of blue or white jeans with a red, black, or green sweater

3. a choice of a small, medium, or large pizza with thin or thick crust and pepperoni, sausage, or Canadian bacon

4. choosing a sedan, hatchback, station wagon, or convertible in white, gray, or red with a manual or automatic transmission

PRACTICE WORKSHEET 14-2

Probability and Percents

There are two red marbles, one green marble, and one yellow marble in a bag.
One marble is chosen. Find the probability that each event will occur.

1. a red marble

2. a yellow marble

3. a red or a green marble

4. a yellow or a green marble

5. *not* a green marble

6. a blue marble

There are two black, four red, three purple, and one orange marker in a box.
One marker is chosen. Find the probability the event will occur.

7. a red marker

8. a black or a purple marker

9. *not* an orange marker

10. a green marker

11. a red, a purple, or an orange marker

12. *not* a red or a purple marker

Each spinner at the right is spun once. Find
the probability of spinning each of the
following. Round to the nearest whole percent.
(Hint: First make a list of the possible
combinations of spins.)

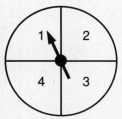 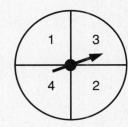

13. a 3 on both spinners

14. a 2 on the first spinner and a 4 on the second spinner

15. a 1 on one spinner and a 3 on the other

16. both numbers the same

17. both numbers less than 4

18. a 3 on exactly one spinner

19. a 3 on at least one spinner

20. one number less than the other

Glencoe Division, Macmillan/McGraw-Hill

PRACTICE WORKSHEET 14-3

Multiplying Probabilities

A bag contains four red, five white, and three blue marbles. Suppose you choose a marble from the bag and then choose another marble without replacing the first one. Find the probability of choosing each event.

1. white both times

2. blue both times

3. red both times

4. same color both times

5. red, then white

6. white, then red

7. white, then blue

8. red, then green

Suppose you choose a marble from the bag described above, replace it, and then choose another. Find the probability of choosing each event.

9. white both times

10. blue both times

11. red both times

12. same color both times

13. red, then white

14. white, then red

15. white, then blue

16. red, then green

Solve.

17. A card is drawn from the deck shown below. Then another card is drawn without replacing the first. What is the probability that the cards drawn will be 2, 3 or 3, 2?

18. A card is selected at random from the group shown below. A second card is drawn without replacing the first. What is the probability that both cards will have odd numbers on them?

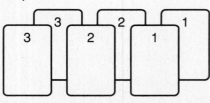

PRACTICE WORKSHEET 14-4

Adding Probabilities

Find each probability. Use the spinner at the right.

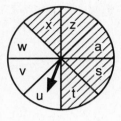

1. P(w or t)

2. P(a consonant or a vowel)

3. P(a vowel or striped)

4. P(a consonant or white)

Find each probability. Use the cards below.

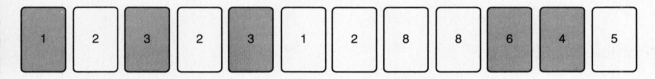

5. P(an odd number or 2)

6. P(3 or 8)

7. P(an even number or white)

8. P(gray or a prime number)

9. P(an odd number or 1)

10. P(an even number or a prime number)

The different color shapes below are placed in a box. One shape is drawn from the box. Find each probability.

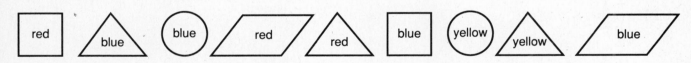

11. P(a triangle or a quadrilateral)

12. P(a red shape or a circle)

13. P(a triangle that is blue)

14. P(a blue shape or a square)

15. P(a red shape or a polygon)

16. P(a yellow shape or a triangle)

PRACTICE WORKSHEET 14-5

Applications: Marketing Research

A company surveyed 120 people about their favorite radio station and the amount of time they listen to the radio each day. The results are shown in the tables below.

Favorite Radio Station	Number of People
KALM	28
KOOL	32
KLAS	15
KRZY	34
none	11

Time Spent Listening to Radio Daily	Number of People
more than 2 h	28
61 min–2 h	30
1 min–1 h	50
0 min	12

Find the probability of a person liking each station best.

1. KOOL

2. KOOL or KRZY

3. not KALM

4. neither KALM nor KOOL

Find the probability of a person most likely listening to the radio for each time.

5. 1 min–1 h

6. more than 1 h

7. 2 h or less

8. not at all

Assuming that the choice of station and the amount of time spent listening are independent, find the probability of each combination of favorite station and time spent listening to the radio each day.

9. KRZY and more than 2 h

10. KALM and 61 min–2 h

11. not KOOL and 1 min–1 h

12. no favorite station and not listening at all

PRACTICE WORKSHEET 14-6

Odds

A die is rolled. Find the odds for each roll.

1. a 6

2. not an odd number

3. a number less than 4

4. a 5 or a 6

5. a 9

6. a 6 or a 1

7. a 4, 3, or 1

8. not a 2

9. a 2 or an odd number

10. a 3 or an 8

Two dice are rolled. Find the odds for each roll.

11. both dice different

12. a 3 and a 5

13. a sum of 12

14. a sum of 7

15. a sum of 5 or 10

16. a sum less than 5

17. a sum of 1

18. *not* a sum of 8

19. a sum of 4 and a 2 on at least one die

20. a sum of 5 and a 3 on one die

Solve.

21. On a TV game show, the contestant is supposed to match the correct price with a prize. If four prices are shown, what are the odds of selecting the correct one at random?

22. If two coins are tossed, what are the odd for both coins landing with the same side up? What are the odds for both coins landing heads?

PRACTICE WORKSHEET 14-7

Problem-Solving Strategy: Using Samples to Predict

Solve. Use the results of the survey below for Exercises 1– 9. The sample is taken from 1,500 students.

1. How many students are in the sample?

2. What is the probability that a student collects baseball cards?

3. Predict how many of the 1,500 students collect baseball cards.

What do you collect?	
Stamps	35
Coins	20
Baseball cards	80
Rocks	15

4. What is the probability that a student collects rocks?

5. Predict how many of the 1,500 students collect rocks.

6. What is the probability that a student collects coins?

7. Predict how many of the 1,500 students collect coins.

8. If there are 30 students in one class, predict how many collect coins.

9. Is it possible that a student will not collect stamps, coins, baseball cards, or rocks?

Solve.

10. In a survey of 200 people in Westville, 150 plan to vote in the town election. What is the probability that a person in Westville will vote?

11. Refer to Exercise 10. If the population of Westville is 14,000, predict how many people will vote.

12. If the television ad that states five out of six people will buy a new toothpaste is correct, what is the probability that your neighbor will buy it?

13. Refer to Exercise 12. If 3,000 supermarket customers are planning to buy toothpaste, predict how many will buy the new toothpaste.

ANSWER KEY

PRACTICE WORKSHEET 1-1

Place Value

Name the place-value position for each digit in 106.3972.

1. the 0 **tens**
2. the 9 **hundredths**
3. the 3 **tenths**
4. the 6 **ones**
5. the 1 **hundreds**
6. the 2 **ten thousandths**

Complete the word name for each number.

7. 547,000
   five hundred forty-seven **thousand**
8. 0.086
   eighty-six **thousandths**
9. 0.159
   one hundred fifty-nine **thousandths**
10. 3.07
    three and seven **hundredths**

Write the number named by the 4 in each number.

11. 14,690 **4,000**
12. 480,000 **400,000**
13. 7.004 **0.004**
14. 18.345 **0.04**

Place the decimal point in each number to show the number named in words.

15. thirty-five hundredths
    035 **0.35**
16. five hundred twenty thousandths
    0520 **0.520**
17. two hundred nine and four tenths
    2094 **209.4**
18. forty-four and four hundredths
    4404 **44.04**

Write in standard form.

19. seventy-two thousand, three   **72,003**
20. three million, five hundred seven thousand, ninety   **3,507,090**
21. forty-three and seven tenths   **43.7**
22. eight and forty-seven thousandths   **8.047**

Glencoe Division, Macmillan/McGraw-Hill

1

PRACTICE WORKSHEET 1-2

Exponents

Write using exponents.

1. $5 \times 5 \times 5$
   5^3
2. $6 \times 6 \times 6 \times 6$
   6^5
3. $9 \times 9 \times 9 \times 9 \times 9 \times 9$
   9^6
4. $7 \times 7 \times 7 \times 7 \times 7 \times 7 \times 7 \times 7$ 7^8
5. $2 \times 2 \times 2 \times 2 \times 2 \times 2 \times 2$ 2^7
6. $1 \times 1 \times 1 \times 1 \times 1$ 1^5

7. 3 squared
   3^2
8. 2 to the fourth power
   2^4
9. 8 cubed
   8^3

Write in standard form.

10. $200 + 30 + 9$
    239
11. $(7 \times 1,000) + (3 \times 10)$
    7,030
12. $(6 \times 10^3) + (5 \times 10^2) + (3 \times 10^0)$
    6,503

Write in expanded form using 10^0, 10^1, 10^2 and so on.

13. 328
    $(3 \times 10^2) + (2 \times 10^1) + (8 \times 10^0)$
14. 5,402
    $(5 \times 10^3) + (4 \times 10^2) + (2 \times 10^0)$
15. 87,001
    $(8 \times 10^4) + (7 \times 10^3) + (1 \times 10^0)$

Write as a product and then find the number named.

16. 5^3
    $5 \times 5 \times 5 = 125$
17. 2^6
    $2 \times 2 \times 2 \times 2 \times 2 \times 2 = 64$
18. 1^4
    $1 \times 1 \times 1 \times 1 = 1$
19. 2^5
    $2 \times 2 \times 2 \times 2 \times 2 = 32$
20. 6^3
    $6 \times 6 \times 6 = 216$
21. 7^2
    $7 \times 7 = 49$
22. 11^2
    $11 \times 11 = 121$
23. 5^2
    $5 \times 5 = 25$
24. 3^2
    $3 \times 3 = 9$
25. 6^2
    $6 \times 6 = 36$
26. 10^3
    $10 \times 10 \times 10 = 1,000$
27. 8^2
    $8 \times 8 = 64$

Solve.

28. Feisty Farlow made a deal to work for a grain company. He worked the first day for one grain of wheat. The second day he worked for two grains of wheat. The third day he worked for four grains of wheat. Each day the amount doubled. Express the number of grains of wheat that Feisty earned on the 10th day as a power.
    2^9

Glencoe Division, Macmillan/McGraw-Hill

2

PRACTICE WORKSHEET 1-3

Comparing Whole Numbers and Decimals

Fill in the blank with >, <, or = to make a true sentence.

1. 6 **<** 60
2. 0.80 **=** 0.8
3. 140 **>** 104
4. 0.72 **<** 0.8
5. 1.5 **=** 1.50
6. 3,200 **>** 3,020
7. 5.23 **<** 5.3
8. 8.9 **>** 8.88
9. 393 **>** 339
10. 989 **<** 998
11. 0.20 **>** 0.02
12. 1.56 **>** 1.55
13. 0.99 **<** 1.00
14. 13.4 **>** 1.43

Order the numbers from least to greatest.

15. 2,041; 2,001; 2,341; 2,011
    2,001; 2,011; 2,041; 2,341
16. 3,342; 3,234; 4,332; 3,432; 2,432
    2,432; 3,234; 3,342; 3,432; 4,332
17. 0.7, 0.67, 0.51, 0.03, 0.07
    0.03, 0.07, 0.51, 0.67, 0.7
18. 0.8, 1.08, 1.8, 0.08, 1.88
    0.08, 0.8, 1.08, 1.8, 1.88
19. 754,004; 75,403; 754,011; 745,004
    75,403; 745,004; 754,004; 754,011
20. 2.12, 1.2, 1.112, 2.121
    1.112, 1.2, 2.12, 2.121
21. 8.91, 8.919, 8.98, 8.989, 8.198
    8.198, 8.91, 8.919, 8.98, 8.989
22. 1.3, 1.03, 1.303, 1.313, 1.033
    1.03, 1.033, 1.3, 1.303, 1.313

Glencoe Division, Macmillan/McGraw-Hill

3

PRACTICE WORKSHEET 1-4

Rounding Whole Numbers and Decimals

Round each number to the nearest whole number.

1. 8.3
   8
2. 7.42
   7
3. 321.68
   322
4. 0.007
   0

Round each number to the nearest thousand.

5. 2,703
   3,000
6. 27,439
   27,000
7. 882
   1,000
8. 6,499
   6,000

Round each number to the nearest tenth.

9. 4.71
   4.7
10. 32.28
    32.3
11. 178.69
    178.7
12. 39.04
    39.0

Round each number to the nearest hundredth.

13. 2.376
    2.38
14. 0.039
    0.04
15. 7.222
    7.22
16. 3.4083
    3.41

Round each number to the underlined place-value position.

17. 6̲48
    650
18. 93.1̲74
    93.17
19. 7.6̲35
    7.64
20. 5̲,298
    5,000
21. 57.7̲99
    57.80
22. 17,8̲62
    17,900
23. 0.00̲81
    0.008
24. 6̲0.519
    61
25. 0.73̲5
    0.74
26. 9̲72
    1,000
27. 201.8̲99
    200
28. 0.9̲999
    1.00

Round each number to the nearest hundredth, tenth, and whole number.

29. 7.893 7.89 / 7.9 / 8
30. 149.0769 149.08 / 149.1 / 149
31. 9.598 9.60 / 9.6 / 10
32. 0.0895 0.09 / 0.1 / 0

Glencoe Division, Macmillan/McGraw-Hill

4

147

Glencoe Division, Macmillan/McGraw-Hill

ANSWER KEY

Name _____ Date _____

PRACTICE WORKSHEET 1-5

Applications: Using Tax Tables

Ten people work for the Xenon Gas Station. The table below shows their taxable income, filing status, federal withholding tax, and whether additional taxes are owed or a refund is due.

Use the tax table at the right to complete the table below.

If line 37 (taxable income) is—		And you are—			
At least	But less than	Single	Married filing jointly	Married filing separately	Head of a household
			Your tax is—		
10,000					
10,000	10,050	1,058	799	1,212	989
10,050	10,100	1,066	806	1,221	997
10,100	10,150	1,074	813	1,230	1,006
10,150	10,200	1,082	820	1,239	1,014
10,200	10,250	1,090	827	1,248	1,023
10,250	10,300	1,098	834	1,257	1,031
10,300	10,350	1,106	841	1,266	1,040
10,350	10,400	1,114	848	1,275	1,048
10,400	10,450	1,122	855	1,284	1,057
10,450	10,500	1,130	862	1,293	1,065
10,500	10,550	1,138	869	1,302	1,074
10,550	10,600	1,146	876	1,313	1,082
10,600	10,650	1,154	883	1,324	1,091
10,650	10,700	1,162	890	1,335	1,099
10,700	10,750	1,170	897	1,346	1,108
10,750	10,800	1,178	904	1,357	1,116

Name	Taxable Income	Filing Status	Federal Tax Withheld	Additional Tax Owed	Amount of Refund
Raul	$10,112	hh	$998	1. $8	none
Paula	$10,762	s	2. $908.95	$269.05	none
Anoki	$10,433	mj	$910	none	3. $55
Lewis	$10,525	4. S	$930	$208.00	none
Shamu	$10,340	ms	5. $1,310	none	$44
Christin	$10,613	6. mj	$900	none	7. $17
Pamela	$10,701	hh	8. $1,056	$52	none
Dan	$10,155	ms	$1,424	9. none	10. $185
Kerry	$10,205	s	11. $1,243	12. none	$153
Mel	$10,111	13. S	$999	$75	14. none

Glencoe Division, Macmillan/McGraw-Hill

5

Name _____ Date _____

PRACTICE WORKSHEET 1-6

Estimating Sums and Differences

Estimate. Answers may vary. Typical answers given.

1.
$$\begin{array}{r} 482 \\ + 890 \\ \hline 1,400 \end{array}$$

2.
$$\begin{array}{r} \$4.37 \\ + 0.93 \\ \hline 5.30 \end{array}$$

3.
$$\begin{array}{r} 34.7 \\ - 0.84 \\ \hline 33.9 \end{array}$$

4.
$$\begin{array}{r} 837 \\ - 359 \\ \hline 400 \end{array}$$

5.
$$\begin{array}{r} 438 \\ 568 \\ + 1,389 \\ \hline 2,400 \end{array}$$

6.
$$\begin{array}{r} 7.33 \\ 40.27 \\ + 0.6 \\ \hline 48.2 \end{array}$$

7.
$$\begin{array}{r} 3,823 \\ 477 \\ + 5,789 \\ \hline 10,100 \end{array}$$

8.
$$\begin{array}{r} 0.27 \\ 16.8 \\ + 0.34 \\ \hline 17.4 \end{array}$$

9.
$$\begin{array}{r} 872 \\ - 586 \\ \hline 300 \end{array}$$

10.
$$\begin{array}{r} \$86.06 \\ - 28.49 \\ \hline \$60 \end{array}$$

11.
$$\begin{array}{r} 0.63 \\ - 0.38 \\ \hline 0.2 \end{array}$$

12.
$$\begin{array}{r} 72,685 \\ - 4,499 \\ \hline 69,000 \end{array}$$

13. $0.89 + 2.3$ 3.2
14. $81 - 18$ 60
15. $7.04 - 0.8$ 6.2

Solve. Round.

16. There are 345 white pages and 783 yellow pages in the local telephone directory. About how many more yellow pages than white pages does the directory contain?
500 pages

17. A truck weighing 6,675 pounds is carrying a load of apples weighing 953 pounds. About how much do the truck and the apples weigh?
7,700 pounds

Solve. Round to the nearest dollar.

18. Lenny bought a shirt for $17.89. About how much change will he receive from a $20 bill? **$2**

19. Judy has $30. Can she afford to buy a belt for $5.67, a skirt for $14.29, and tights for $13.95? **no**

Glencoe Division, Macmillan/McGraw-Hill

6

Name _____ Date _____

PRACTICE WORKSHEET 1-7

Estimating Products and Quotients.

Estimate.

1. 5.03×9.37
   45
2. 112×694
   70,000
3. 87.7×18.3
   1,800

4. 0.803×483.5
   400
5. 96×58
   6,000
6. 375.5×28.1
   12,000

7.
$$\begin{array}{r} 490 \\ \times 7 \\ \hline 3,500 \end{array}$$
8.
$$\begin{array}{r} 32.9 \\ \times 68 \\ \hline 2,100 \end{array}$$
9.
$$\begin{array}{r} 7,288 \\ \times 315 \\ \hline 2,100,000 \end{array}$$

10.
$$\begin{array}{r} 5,399 \\ \times 0.79 \\ \hline 4,000 \end{array}$$
11.
$$\begin{array}{r} 7,831 \\ \times 4.8 \\ \hline 40,000 \end{array}$$
12.
$$\begin{array}{r} 3,900 \\ \times 49 \\ \hline 200,000 \end{array}$$

13. $358 \div 91$
   4
14. $735.4 \div 76.9$
   9
15. $7,175 \div 9$
   800

16. $1,680 \div 38$
   40
17. $5,139 \div 194$
   25
18. $2,000 \div 6.9$
   300

19. $8\overline{)395}$ 50
20. $7.2\overline{)50.2}$ 7
21. $47\overline{)97}$ 2

22. $79\overline{)55,794}$ 700
23. $41\overline{)\$15.85}$ $0.40
24. $8.5\overline{)\$25.63}$ $3.00

25. $58\overline{)5,360}$ 90
26. $29\overline{)2,000}$ 70
27. $4.8\overline{)345.9}$ 70

Glencoe Division, Macmillan/McGraw-Hill

7

Name _____ Date _____

PRACTICE WORKSHEET 1-8

Problem Solving Strategy: Matrix Logic

Use the clues to complete a matrix table for each problem below.

1. George, Gene, and Gina each have a favorite vegetable. None of the vegetables is the same. The three vegetables are broccoli, carrots, and peas. Use the table and the clues below to find out who likes which vegetable.
   a. The boys like green vegetables.
   b. Gene's vegetable is not round.

	broc.	carrots	peas
George	N	N	Y
Gene	Y	N	N
Gina	N	Y	N

2. Michael, Mandy, Mario, and Maude all like different flavors of ice cream. Use a table to find out which person likes each flavor of ice cream best. The flavors are vanilla, chocolate, butterscotch, and strawberry.
   a. Michael does not like fruit-flavored ice cream.
   b. Mandy likes butterscotch.
   c. Mario does not like vanilla or chocolate.
   d. Maude does not like vanilla.

	van.	choc.	butter.	straw.
Michael	Y	N	N	N
Mandy	N	N	Y	N
Mario	N	N	N	Y
Maude	N	Y	N	N

3. Cathy, Carlos, Charles, and Carrie all have favorite numbers that are different from one another. The numbers are 2, 3, 5, and 7, but are not necessarily in that order. Use a table to find out which person has which favorite number.
   a. Carrie's favorite number is less than 6 and greater than 2.
   b. Cathy likes the number that divides into 10 evenly.
   c. Carlos likes the greatest number.
   d. Charles likes the even number.

	2	3	5	7
Cathy	N	N	Y	N
Carrie	N	Y	N	N
Carlos	N	N	N	Y
Charles	Y	N	N	N

4. Four friends, Fred, Flora, Frank and Fran each have different phone area codes. The area codes they have are 201, 203, 212, and 213. Use the table to find each friend's area code.
   a. The sum of the digits in Fred's area code is not 5.
   b. No girl has an area code the sum of whose digits is divisible by 3.
   c. There is no 0 in Fred's or Fran's area code.

	201	203	212	213
Fred	N	N	N	Y
Flora	N	Y	N	N
Frank	Y	N	N	N
Fran	N	N	Y	N

Glencoe Division, Macmillan/McGraw-Hill

8

ANSWER KEY

Name _____ Date _____

PRACTICE WORKSHEET 1-9

Order of Operations

Name the operation that should be done first.

1. $7 + 6 \div 2$ division
2. $8 \times 3^2 \div 3$ find square
3. $2 \times (12 - 4)$ subtraction
4. $6 + 8 - 3$ addition
5. $16 \div 4 \times 2^2$ find square
6. $63 \div (4 + 3)$ addition
7. $[(2 + 3) \times 7] - 4^2$ addition
8. $52 \times [6 + (14 \div 2)]$ division

Find the value of each expression.

9. $63 \div (4 + 5)$ 7
10. $12 + 7 \times 3^2$ 75
11. $4 \times 5 - 3$ 17
12. $24 \div 6 \times 2^2$ 16
13. $24 \div (6 \times 2)$ 2
14. $48 \div 6 + 2$ 4
15. $3^2 + 9 \times 5$ 54
16. $7 - 3 + 9$ 13
17. $52 \div 4 + 9$ 22
18. $8 + 12 \div 4$ 11
19. $21 - 6 - 4$ 11
20. $(3^2 + 5) \times 7$ 98
21. $(8 + 12) \div 4$ 5
22. $21 - (6 - 4)$ 19
23. $(3 + 5) \times 7$ 56
24. $48 \div 8 + 4$ 50
25. $(26 - 6) - 4^2$ 4
26. $3 + 5 \times 7$ 38
27. $27 \div (2 \times 4 + 1)$ 3
28. $10^2 + (16 + 9 \times 7)$ 179
29. $[36 \div (5 + 8 \div 2) + 1]$ 5
30. $18 + [15 - (8 - 1)] \times 3$ 42
31. $[(6 + 3) \times 4] + [7 \times 2 - 2]$ 3
32. $[2 + (3 - 1)] \times [(8 - 6)^2 \times 3]$ 48

Write an expression and solve.

33. Jane packed 6 hams in a shipping crate. Each ham weighs 5 pounds. The crate weighs 2 pounds. How much does the total package weigh?
$(6 \times 5) + 2$; 32 pounds

34. Martha wrote checks to each of her 7 grandchildren. The older three received $15 each. The others received $10. What was the total of Martha's checks?
$(\$15 \times 3) + (\$10 \times 4)$; \$85

35. Stella correctly answered 19 problems on a math test. Six of the problems were worth 5 points each. The others were worth 4 points each. What was Stella's score?
$(6 \times 5) + (13 \times 4)$; 82 points

36. Manuel sold 72 daily newspapers at 35¢ each and 75 Sunday newspapers at $1.25 each. What was his total income?
$(72 \times 35¢) + (75 \times \$1.25)$; \$118.95

Name _____ Date _____

PRACTICE WORKSHEET 1-10

Evaluating Expressions

Find the value of each expression.

1. $16 - 4 \times 3 + 2$ 6
2. $15 + 3^2$ 24
3. $15 \div 3 + 4 \times 8$ 37
4. $4 \times (9 + 3)$ 48
5. $4 \times 2^2 - 2 \times 2$ 12
6. $5^2 - 3(5) - 8$ 2

Find the value of each expression if n = 3.

7. $6n$ 18
8. $4(n + 5)$ 32
9. $4n - 12$ 0
10. $(6 - n)^2 + 13$ 22
11. $\dfrac{n^2 + 6}{3}$ 5
12. $8(16 - n)$ 104

Find the value of each expression if t = 3, u = 2, and v = 5.

13. $5t - v$ 10
14. $5t - u^2$ 11
15. $t + 3u - v$ 4
16. $(v - u)^2 + t$ 12
17. $3tv + 8u$ 61
18. $t(v - u)$ 9

Find the value of each expression if a = 5, b = 3, and c = 7.

19. $a^2 + c^2$ 74
20. $6b^2$ 54
21. $a^2 - b$ 22
22. $a^2 - b^2$ 16
23. $(a + c)^2$ 144
24. $5(a - b)$ 10

Solve.

25. A science lab is in the shape of a rectangle. The lab is 32 feet long by 25 feet wide. Use $P = 2(l + w)$ to find the perimeter of the lab.
114 feet

26. A courtyard at a high school is in the shape of a square. The length of each side, s, is 12 meters. Use $A = s^2$ to find the area of the courtyard.
144 square meters

27. The math club uses a phone tree to get messages out. The president calls two members, who each call two others, who each call two others, and so on. How many are called at the fourth level?
16

28. Write a formula to find the perimeter of your math classroom. Then find the perimeter.
Answers will vary. Should include the lengths of all sides.

Name _____ Date _____

PRACTICE WORKSHEET 1-11

Solving Equations Using Addition and Subtraction

Solve each equation. Check each solution.

1. $9 + s = 14$ $s = 5$
2. $4 + t = 5$ $t = 1$
3. $22 - r = 15$ $r = 7$
4. $18 - a = 6$ $a = 12$
5. $22 + 4 = b$ $b = 26$
6. $x + 9 = 9$ $x = 0$
7. $(6 + 2) = y$ $y = 8$
8. $9 + r = 26$ $r = 17$
9. $36 - 0 = a$ $a = 36$
10. $w - 30 = 2$ $w = 32$
11. $196 + 14 = b$ $b = 210$
12. $24 - p = 19$ $p = 5$
13. $20.8 + g = 21.8$ $g = 1$
14. $w = 4.2 + 1.55$ $w = 5.75$
15. $7.68 + l = 32$ $l = 24.32$
16. $t + 4.5 = 9$ $t = 4.5$
17. $4.019 = t - 6.11$ $t = 10.129$
18. $8.06 - d = 6.543$ $d = 1.517$

Write an equation. Then solve.

19. Ten increased by x is 17. What is the value of x?
$10 + x = 17$, $x = 7$

20. Thirteen decreased by r is 9. What is the value of r?
$13 - r = 9$, $r = 4$

21. Twelve less than t is 13. What is the value of t?
$t - 12 = 13$, $t = 25$

22. Five more than p is 7.3. What is the value of p?
$p + 5 = 7.3$, $p = 2.3$

Solve. Use an equation.

23. When a number is added to 12, the result is 27. Find the number.
$12 + n = 27$, 15

24. The difference of 6 and a number is 72. Find the number.
$n - 6 = 72$, 78

25. When a number is subtracted from 12, the result is 9. Find the number.
$12 - n = 9$, 3

26. When 15 is subtracted from a number, the result is 7.5. Find the number.
$n - 15 = 7.5$, 22.5

Name _____ Date _____

PRACTICE WORKSHEET 1-12

Solving Equations Using Multiplication and Division

Solve each equation. Check each solution.

1. $9 \times s = 54$ $s = 6$
2. $4t = 20$ $t = 5$
3. $\dfrac{12}{r} = 6$ $r = 2$
4. $\dfrac{18}{a} = 6$ $a = 3$
5. $2.5n = 10$ $n = 4$
6. $\dfrac{x}{9} = 9$ $x = 81$
7. $0.3p = 3$ $p = 10$
8. $9 \times r = 27$ $r = 3$
9. $\dfrac{36}{n} = 4$ $n = 9$
10. $5q = 0.25$ $q = 0.05$
11. $\dfrac{196}{14} = b$ $b = 14$
12. $24 \times p = 19.2$ $p = 0.8$
13. $\dfrac{20.8}{g} = 1.3$ $g = 16$
14. $3m = 0.09$ $m = 0.03$
15. $0.5 = \dfrac{p}{2}$ $p = 1$
16. $10t = 9$ $t = 0.9$
17. $0.3r = 0.9$ $r = 3$
18. $0.1 = \dfrac{x}{7}$ $x = 0.7$

Write an equation. Then solve.

19. Eleven multiplied by r is 99. What is the value of r?   9

20. A number divided by 4 is 10. What is the number?   40

21. The product of n and 0.7 is 1.4. What is the value of n?   2

22. Twelve divided by 2.4 is p. What is the value of p?   5

Write an equation. Then solve.

23. When a number is multiplied by 12, the result is 60. Find the number.
$12n = 60$, $n = 5$

24. The product of 6 and a number is 72. Find the number.
$6n = 72$, $n = 12$

25. When a number is divided by 12, the result is 9. Find the number.
$\dfrac{n}{12} = 9$, $n = 108$

26. When 15 is divided by a number, the result is 0.3. Find the number.
$\dfrac{15}{n} = 0.3$, $n = 50$

ANSWER KEY

PRACTICE WORKSHEET 1-13

Problem Solving: Write an Equation

Choose the correct equation to solve each problem. Then solve.

1. On Tuesday at Casa Burrito 136 orders of chicken fajitas were sold and 154 orders of shrimp fajitas were sold. How many orders of fajitas were sold? **290 fajitas**
   - a. $154 - 136 = y$
   - b.) $154 + 136 = y$ $y = 290$

2. Tortillas are packed 50 to a box. How many tortillas are in 10 boxes? **500 tortillas**
   - a.) $50 \times 10 = z$
   - b. $50 + 10 = z$ $z = 500$

Write an equation to solve each problem. Then solve.

3. An order of chicken fajitas costs $6.75. How much do 13 orders cost?
   $13 \times \$6.75 = n$, $n = \$87.75$

4. To make the day's guacamolé José needs 39 more avocados. He has 42 avocados. How many avocados does the recipe call for?
   $39 + 42 = n$, $n = 81$

5. Mr. Serra spent $15.75 for lunch for himself and his four children. If everyone had the same lunch, how much did each lunch cost?
   $\$15.75 \div 5 = n$, $n = \$3.15$

6. Mr. Serra gave the waiter a $20 bill for the lunches. How much should he receive in change?
   $\$20 - \$15.75 = n$, $n = \$4.25$

7. Mr. Serra left a tip of $3.00. How much did lunch and tip cost in all?
   $\$15.75 + \$3 = n$, $n = \$18.75$

8. If Mr. Serra takes his children out to lunch once a month and spends $15.75 plus a $3 tip each time, how much does he spend in a year?
   $(\$15.75 + \$3) \times 12 = n$, $n = \$225$

9. A combination platter at Casa Burrito has 738 calories. If Carlos has a combination platter and wants to limit himself to 1,500 calories a day, how many more calories can he consume that day?
   $1,500 - 738 = n$, $n = 762$

10. A glass of fruit juice contains 154 calories. If Carlos has a glass with his combination platter how many calories will he have had at Casa Burrito?
    $738 + 154 = n$, $n = 892$

PRACTICE WORKSHEET 2-1

Adding Whole Numbers

Add.

1. $\begin{array}{r} 48 \\ +\ 6 \\ \hline 54 \end{array}$	2. $\begin{array}{r} 24 \\ +\ 69 \\ \hline 93 \end{array}$	3. $\begin{array}{r} 487 \\ +\ 215 \\ \hline 702 \end{array}$	4. $\begin{array}{r} 396 \\ +\ 77 \\ \hline 473 \end{array}$	5. $\begin{array}{r} 543 \\ +\ 8 \\ \hline 551 \end{array}$
6. $\begin{array}{r} 936 \\ +\ 4,173 \\ \hline 5,109 \end{array}$	7. $\begin{array}{r} 8,318 \\ +\ 1,236 \\ \hline 9,554 \end{array}$	8. $\begin{array}{r} 3,807 \\ +\ 4,524 \\ \hline 8,331 \end{array}$	9. $\begin{array}{r} 7,565 \\ +\ 936 \\ \hline 8,501 \end{array}$	10. $\begin{array}{r} 48 \\ +\ 6,154 \\ \hline 6,202 \end{array}$
11. $\begin{array}{r} 1,346 \\ +\ 56,672 \\ \hline 58,018 \end{array}$	12. $\begin{array}{r} 38,416 \\ +\ 2,618 \\ \hline 41,034 \end{array}$	13. $\begin{array}{r} 73,281 \\ +\ 15,765 \\ \hline 89,046 \end{array}$	14. $\begin{array}{r} 797 \\ +\ 39,044 \\ \hline 39,841 \end{array}$	15. $\begin{array}{r} 43,167 \\ +\ 68 \\ \hline 43,235 \end{array}$

16. $5,783 + 1,764$ 7,547
17. $5,383 + 279$ 5,662
18. $3,088 + 25,921$ 29,009

19. $52,675 + 3,678$ 56,353
20. $493 + 38,267$ 38,760
21. $72,786 + 45,439$ 118,225

Solve. Use the chart.

22. How many immigrants came to the U.S. during 1921–1940? **4,635,640 immigrants**

23. How many immigrants came to the U.S. during 1941–1960? **3,550,518 immigrants**

24. How many immigrants came to the U.S. during 1961–1980? **7,815,091 immigrants**

Immigrants to the U.S. from all countries	
1921–1930	4,107,209
1931–1940	528,431
1941–1950	1,035,039
1951–1960	2,515,479
1961–1970	3,321,777
1971–1980	4,493,314

PRACTICE WORKSHEET 2-2

Adding Decimals

Add.

1. $\begin{array}{r} 0.3 \\ +\ 0.6 \\ \hline 0.9 \end{array}$	2. $\begin{array}{r} 0.4 \\ +\ 0.7 \\ \hline 1.1 \end{array}$	3. $\begin{array}{r} 0.7 \\ +\ 0.2 \\ \hline 0.9 \end{array}$	4. $\begin{array}{r} 0.9 \\ +\ 0.8 \\ \hline 1.7 \end{array}$
5. $\begin{array}{r} 7.3 \\ +\ 1.8 \\ \hline 9.1 \end{array}$	6. $\begin{array}{r} 3.4 \\ +\ 2.5 \\ \hline 5.9 \end{array}$	7. $\begin{array}{r} 5.6 \\ +\ 1.2 \\ \hline 6.8 \end{array}$	8. $\begin{array}{r} 7.4 \\ +\ 4.7 \\ \hline 12.1 \end{array}$
9. $\begin{array}{r} 0.62 \\ +\ 0.4 \\ \hline 1.02 \end{array}$	10. $\begin{array}{r} 0.13 \\ +\ 0.9 \\ \hline 1.03 \end{array}$	11. $\begin{array}{r} \$0.78 \\ +\ 0.43 \\ \hline \$1.21 \end{array}$	12. $\begin{array}{r} \$0.98 \\ +\ 0.12 \\ \hline \$1.10 \end{array}$
13. $\begin{array}{r} 2.076 \\ +\ 1.34 \\ \hline 3.416 \end{array}$	14. $\begin{array}{r} 3.7 \\ +\ 1.609 \\ \hline 5.309 \end{array}$	15. $\begin{array}{r} 5.8 \\ +\ 14.312 \\ \hline 20.112 \end{array}$	16. $\begin{array}{r} 12.006 \\ +\ 4.3 \\ \hline 16.306 \end{array}$
17. $\begin{array}{r} 3.6 \\ 4.9 \\ +\ 21.4 \\ \hline 29.9 \end{array}$	18. $\begin{array}{r} \$4.78 \\ 6.20 \\ +\ 5.16 \\ \hline \$16.14 \end{array}$	19. $\begin{array}{r} 0.1 \\ 4.08 \\ +\ 19.164 \\ \hline 23.344 \end{array}$	20. $\begin{array}{r} 9.1 \\ 22.006 \\ +\ 40.07 \\ \hline 71.176 \end{array}$

21. $\$16.49 + \$26$ $\$42.49$
22. $7.439 + 0.88$ 8.319
23. $0.564 + 19.7$ 20.264

24. $0.976 + 23.4$ 24.376
25. $\$58 + 36¢$ $\$58.36$
26. $6.325 + 29$ 35.325

Solve.

27. Nam's speed-reading times are 2.1 minutes, 2.06 minutes, 1.98 minutes, and 1.9 minutes. What is his total reading time?
    8.04 minutes

28. Tina orders a hamburger for $1.59, salad for $0.89, and juice for $0.69. What is her total bill?
    $3.17

PRACTICE WORKSHEET 2-3

Subtracting Whole Numbers

Subtract.

1. $\begin{array}{r} 58 \\ -\ 32 \\ \hline 26 \end{array}$	2. $\begin{array}{r} 86 \\ -\ 41 \\ \hline 45 \end{array}$	3. $\begin{array}{r} 600 \\ -\ 407 \\ \hline 193 \end{array}$	4. $\begin{array}{r} 703 \\ -\ 76 \\ \hline 627 \end{array}$	5. $\begin{array}{r} 822 \\ -\ 243 \\ \hline 579 \end{array}$
6. $\begin{array}{r} 790 \\ -\ 135 \\ \hline 655 \end{array}$	7. $\begin{array}{r} 492 \\ -\ 359 \\ \hline 133 \end{array}$	8. $\begin{array}{r} 308 \\ -\ 126 \\ \hline 182 \end{array}$	9. $\begin{array}{r} 853 \\ -\ 247 \\ \hline 606 \end{array}$	10. $\begin{array}{r} 178 \\ -\ 159 \\ \hline 19 \end{array}$
11. $\begin{array}{r} 326 \\ -\ 89 \\ \hline 237 \end{array}$	12. $\begin{array}{r} 271 \\ -\ 225 \\ \hline 46 \end{array}$	13. $\begin{array}{r} 496 \\ -\ 351 \\ \hline 145 \end{array}$	14. $\begin{array}{r} 827 \\ -\ 604 \\ \hline 223 \end{array}$	15. $\begin{array}{r} 965 \\ -\ 745 \\ \hline 220 \end{array}$

16. $\begin{array}{r} 3,451 \\ -\ 1,524 \\ \hline 1,927 \end{array}$
17. $\begin{array}{r} 1,460 \\ -\ 188 \\ \hline 1,272 \end{array}$
18. $\begin{array}{r} 7,285 \\ -\ 3,175 \\ \hline 4,110 \end{array}$

19. $\begin{array}{r} 24,002 \\ -\ 16,126 \\ \hline 7,876 \end{array}$
20. $\begin{array}{r} 5,100 \\ -\ 3,405 \\ \hline 1,695 \end{array}$
21. $\begin{array}{r} 47,316 \\ -\ 27,213 \\ \hline 20,103 \end{array}$

22. $5,208 - 105$ 5,103
23. $3,642 - 2,234$ 1,408
24. $4,622 - 3,784$ 838

Solve.

25. Maureen needs $600 for the down payment on a computer. She has saved $336 already. How much does she still need to save for the down payment?
    $264

26. Yuri took a $20 bill with him to the ball game. He paid $7.50 at the gate for his ticket. He bought snacks for $5.65 and a program for $2.25. How much did he have left?
    $4.60

Name _____ Date _____

PRACTICE WORKSHEET 2-4

Subtracting Decimals
Subtract.

1. 8.4 − 3.3 **5.1**	2. 7.3 − 5.4 **1.9**	3. 8 − 3.1 **4.9**	4. 0.6 − 0.21 **0.39**
5. 0.41 − 0.17 **0.24**	6. $0.86 − 0.17 **$0.69**	7. $10.85 − 2.17 **$8.68**	8. 0.13 − 0.07 **0.06**
9. 0.7 − 0.36 **0.34**	10. 0.727 − 0.451 **0.276**	11. 1.61 − 0.9 **0.71**	12. $10.02 − 0.88 **$9.14**
13. 0.43 − 0.39 **0.04**	14. 6.03 − 0.13 **5.9**	15. $6.70 − 1.42 **$5.28**	16. $5.00 − 2.76 **$2.24**
17. 0.310 − 0.042 **0.268**	18. $75.86 − 1.09 **$74.77**	19. 63,508.76 − 51,429.08 **12,079.68**	20. 2.0003 − 0.08 **1.9203**

21. 11.680 − 4.23 **7.45** 22. 8.42 − 5.526 **2.894**

23. Subtract $22.48 from $56.35. **$33.87**

24. Find the difference of 296.03 and 84.007. **212.023**

Solve.

25. The class collects $19.32 for a holiday project. They need $23.50. How much more must they collect? **$4.18**

26. Connie has 20 milliliters of sulfuric acid. Her experiment calls for 1.6 milliliters. How many milliliters will Connie have left? **18.4 mL**

17

Name _____ Date _____

PRACTICE WORKSHEET 2-5

Applications: Checking Accounts

Complete the balance column to find the amount of money Jennifer Chase has left in her checking account on April 30.

	NUMBER	DATE	DESCRIPTION OF TRANSACTION	PAYMENT/DEBIT (−)	DEPOSIT/CREDIT (+)	BALANCE
						$1231 07
1.	201	4/1	Groden's Grocery	103.82		1127 25
2.	201	4/4	Big Al's Autos	111.26		1015 99
3.	203	4/7	Mickey's Cuisine	72.25		943 74
4.	204	4/8	Wasco Telephone Company	201.44		742 30
5.		4/9	deposit	—	473.53	1215 83
6.	205	4/10	A & T Insurance	386.89		828 94
7.	206	4/11	Wasco Gas	75.53		753 41
8.	207	4/11	Electric Company	195.40		558 01
9.	208	4/12	Mortgage	521.57		36 44
10.		4/12	deposit		713.98	750 42
11.	209	4/19	Loan	92.75		657 67
12.	210	4/21	Darlene's Department Store	118.65		539 02
13.	211	4/21	Super Sundry	5.00		534 02
14.		4/21	deposit		428.60	962 62
15.	212	4/23	Hiri's Furniture	219.74		742 88
16.	213	4/23	City of Charlesville	123.90		618 98
17.	214	4/24	Shot Outlet	78.65		540 33
18.		4/24	deposit	—	628.35	1168 68
19.	215	4/25	Frank's Finer Foods	77.78		1090 90
20.	216	4/25	Pamela Beauty Salon	35.40		1055 50
21.	217	4/28	Buck's Garage	187.65		867 85
22.	218	4/28	Galori& Airlines	213.14		654 71
23.	219	4/30	Kelley's Kennel	97.80		556 91

18

Name _____ Date _____

PRACTICE WORKSHEET 2-6

Arithmetic Sequences

Write the next three numbers in each sequence.

1. 18, 20, 22, **24**, **26**, **28**
2. 54, 48, 42, **36**, **30**, **24**
3. 0.4, 2.4, 4.4, **6.4**, **8.4**, **10.4**
4. 45, 57, 69, **81**, **93**, **105**
5. 25.3, 22, 18.7, **15.4**, **12.1** **8.8**
6. 8.9, 8.5, 8.1, **7.7**, **7.3**, **6.9**
7. 5, 11, 17, 23, **29**, **35**, **41**
8. 11, 15, 19, 23, **27**, **31**, **35**
9. 6, 9, 12, 15, **18**, **21**, **24**
10. 2.1, 2.3, 2.5, 2.7, **2.9**, **3.1**, **3.3**
11. 3.6, 3.1, 2.6, 2.1, **1.6**, **1.1**, **0.6**
12. 8, 27, 46, 65, **84**, **103**, **122**
13. 50, 42, 34, 26, **18**, **10**, **2**
14. 20.6, 21.7, 22.8, 23.9, **25.0** **26.1** **27.2**
15. 3.5, 70, 10.5, 14, **17.5** **21** **24.5**
16. 65, 56, 47, 38, **29**, **20**, **11**

State whether each sequence is arithmetic. If it is, write the next three terms. If is not, write no.

17. 3, 9, 27, 81,... **no**
18. 4, 34, 64, 94,... **124, 154, 184**
19. 21.3, 24.3, 30.3, 33.3,... **no**
20. 4.5, 9, 13.5, 18,... **22.5, 27, 31.5, 36**

Copy and complete each arithmetic sequence.

21. 12, 20, **28**, 36, **44**, **52**
22. 20.5, **23**, 25.5, 28, **30.5**, **33**

19

Name _____ Date _____

PRACTICE WORKSHEET 2-7

Problem-Solving Strategy:
Choosing the Method of Computation

Solve each problem. State the method of computation used.

1. Lisa is ordering sporting goods equipment from a catalog. She orders gym shoes for $68.95, two wrist bands for $3.95 each, a volley-ball for $18.49, and a jersey for $25.95. What is the total amount of Lisa's order?
$121.29; calculator

2. Warren is planning a trip to Funworld with his friends. Warren knows that the entrance fee is $5 and that he will go on about 10 rides. The rides cost between $2 and $3 each. He will buy lunch, some snacks, and maybe a souvenir, too. How much money should Warren take to Funworld?
Possible answer: about $50; estimate

3. Two classes at Lincoln School are raising money for new science equipment for the school. Twenty-five students in one class collected, on the average, $20 each. Twenty students in another class collected an average of $25 each. How much money was raised by the two classes?
$1,000; mental math

4. On his last bank statement, Mark's checking account showed a balance of $324.88. Since then, he has made withdrawals of $30, $50, and $30, and deposits of $134.62 and $208.03. What is the current balance in Mark's account?
$557.53; calculator

5. If Becky saves $400, she can buy a mountain bike. She has already saved $252. She figures that if she saves $37.50 a week from her baby-sitting job for the next 5 weeks, she will have enough money. Is Becky right? Explain.
yes; possible answer: estimation and mental math

6. John wants a motorcycle that costs $2,195. He has saved $468.42 thus far. If he can save $47 a week, how many weeks will it take him to save the money he needs?
37 weeks; calculator

7. Use each of the digits 2, 3, 4, and 5 only once. Find two 2-digit numbers that will give the least possible answer when multiplied.
24 x 35; calculator or paper and pencil

8. A bicycle shop contains 48 bicycles and tricycles. If there is a total of 108 wheels, how many bicycles and how tricycles are in the store?
36 bicycles, 12 tricycles; estimation, number sense, paper and pencil

20

151

ANSWER KEY

Name _____ **Date** _____

PRACTICE WORKSHEET 2-8

Perimeter

Find the perimeter of each figure.

1. 8 m → **32 m**
2. 12 in. → **36 in.**
3. 8 cm, 8 cm, 5 cm, 10 cm → **31 cm**
4. 20 ft, 60 ft → **160 ft**
5. 12 mi, 15 mi, 10 mi, 10 mi, 20 mi → **67 mi**
6. 12 ft, 10 ft, 13 ft, 13 ft, 12 ft, 10 ft → **70 ft**
7. 30 cm, 40 cm, 50 cm → **120 cm**
8. 12.4 m, 12.4 m, 15.2 m, 21.6 m → **61.6 m**
9. 81 ft → **32.4 ft**
10. 8 cm, 10.5 cm → **37 cm**
11. 4.2 m, 4.9 m, 2.1 m, 2 m, 7.7 m → **20.9 m**
12. 8 m, 13 m → **42 m**

Solve.

13. The Parker family's backyard is rectangular, measuring 45 feet by 60 feet. What is the perimeter?
210 ft

14. George has 100 feet of fencing. If he fences a square garden, how long is each side?
25 ft

Glencoe Division, Macmillan/McGraw-Hill

21

Name _____ **Date** _____

PRACTICE WORKSHEET 2-9

Problem Solving: Identifying the Necessary Facts

If the problem has the necessary facts, solve. State any missing or extra facts.

1. Marcia earns $8.10 per hour. Each paycheck she puts $25 toward the purchase of U.S. Savings Bonds and $20 into her savings account. If Marcia gets paid every two weeks, how much will she save in a year?
$1,170; earns $8.10 an hour — extra

2. Brad has a checking account balance of $832.76. He just wrote check #235 to his landlord for $290 to pay the rent for March and check #236 to the electric company for $32.15. What is Brad's new checking account balance?
$510.61; check #235, 236 — extra

3. Charlie had the following payroll deductions last week: State Tax $52.18, Federal Tax $75.13, Health Insurance $5.76, Union Dues $8.50, FICA Tax $32.43, and City Tax $9.12. What were Charlie's total deductions for taxes?
$168.86; health insurance, union dues — extra

4. The Lopez family has a monthly income of $2,450. Each month they pay $490 for rent, $550 for food, $42 for electricity, $90 for entertainment, and $70 for transportation. The remaining money goes to savings and travel. How much do they spend on travel? Missing: amount saved each month

5. Ralph's paycheck was $276.82 after $137.28 in deductions. He deposited the check in his checking account. He also withdrew $25 in cash and wrote a $43.87 check for groceries. How much money was left in Ralph's account? Missing: beginning checking balance

6. Sherrie's bank statement shows a balance of $628.97 in her checking account. She wrote 15 checks, but 3 checks totaling $153 are not included on this statement. What is Sherrie's correct checking account balance?
$475.97; 15 checks, 3 checks — extra

7. The Foster family pays $520 rent each month. They average $130 per month for utilities (gas, electric, water, and telephone). They have lived in this house for 3 years. At this rate, how much rent do they pay in a year?
$6,240; $130 utilities, 3 yr — extra

8. Gail and George budget their monthly household income as follows: $650 for housing, $700 for food, 10% for savings, $50 for transportation, and the rest for miscellaneous expenses. How much money do they save in a month?
Missing: monthly income

9. Carmen puts hair care, cleaning, and new clothes in her monthly budget for clothing. Her total monthly budget is $850, of which $120 goes for clothing. Permanents cost $26 and she bought a $50 dress last week. What is Carmen's monthly budget for clothing?
$120; total budget of $850, permanent $26, dress $50 — extra

10. Pam is paid weekly at the bank where she works. She gets a gross income of $21,580 per year and has weekly deductions of $135.27. What are Pam's total deductions for a year?
$7,034.04; gross income $21,580 — extra.

Glencoe Division, Macmillan/McGraw-Hill

22

Name _____ **Date** _____

PRACTICE WORKSHEET 3-1

Multiplying Whole Numbers

Multiply.

1. 49 × 8 = **392**
2. $64 × 7 = **$448**
3. 97 × 6 = **582**
4. 108 × 5 = **540**
5. $231 × 9 = **$2,079**
6. $735 × 6 = **$4,410**
7. 2,431 × 5 = **12,155**
8. 50 × 12 = **600**
9. $87 × 23 = **$2,001**
10. 92 × 37 = **3,404**
11. 465 × 30 = **13,950**
12. $721 × 20 = **$14,420**
13. $409 × 31 = **$12,679**
14. 657 × 26 = **17,082**
15. 582 × 34 = **19,788**
16. 6,432 × 30 = **192,960**
17. $2,759 × 50 = **$137,950**
18. 3,506 × 24 = **84,144**
19. $5,720 × 32 = **$183,040**
20. $9,874 × 46 = **$454,204**
21. 732 × 400 = **292,800**
22. $694 × 500 = **$347,000**
23. 503 × 307 = **154,421**
24. $620 × 805 = **$499,100**
25. 756 × 327 = **247,212**
26. 506 × 481 = **243,386**
27. 2,407 × 303 = **729,321**
28. $6,409 × 342 = **$2,191,878**

Solve.

29. If a car travels at a constant speed of 55 miles per hour, how far will it travel in 6 hours?
330 mi

30. Juan is reading a book that has 16 chapters. Each chapter has 23 pages. How many pages are in the book?
368 pages

Glencoe Division, Macmillan/McGraw-Hill

23

Name _____ **Date** _____

PRACTICE WORKSHEET 3-2

Multiplying Decimals

Multiply.

1. 0.7 × 3 = **2.1**
2. 2.1 × 9 = **18.9**
3. 7.87 × 6 = **47.22**
4. 0.46 × 7 = **3.22**
5. 0.3 × 0.4 = **0.12**
6. 0.8 × 0.4 = **0.32**
7. 24 × 0.3 = **7.2**
8. 0.71 × 0.2 = **0.142**
9. 0.5 × 0.7 = **0.35**
10. 0.9 × 0.6 = **0.54**
11. 0.74 × 0.3 = **0.222**
12. 0.36 × 0.8 = **0.288**
13. 1.44 × 0.6 = **0.864**
14. 5.27 × 0.7 = **3.689**
15. 2.86 × 0.04 = **0.1144**
16. 0.329 × 0.35 = **0.11515**
17. 5.06 × 1.2 = **6.072**
18. 71.4 × 2.9 = **207.06**
19. 7.64 × 0.29 = **2.2156**
20. 5.28 × 0.52 = **2.7456**
21. 7.24 × 5.9 = **42.716**
22. 0.114 × 0.89 = **0.10146**
23. 6.75 × 9.7 = **65.475**
24. 0.837 × 0.56 = **0.46872**

Solve.

25. Marie travels 5.6 miles per hour on her bike. If she rides for 1.25 hours, how far does she ride?
7 miles

26. Almonds are $1.78 per pound. How much change does Boris receive if he pays for 1.5 pounds with a $5 bill?
$2.33

Glencoe Division, Macmillan/McGraw-Hill

24

152

Glencoe Division, Macmillan/McGraw-Hill

ANSWER KEY

PRACTICE WORKSHEET 3-3

Applications: Buying on Credit

Complete the table.

Cash Price	Down Payment	Monthly Payment	Number of Months	Total Cost	Finance Charge
$366	$10	$35	12	1. $430	2. $64
$900	$100	$75	12	3. $1,000	4. $100
$1,800	$250	$50	36	5. $2,050	6. $250
$6,500	$1,250	$164	36	7. $7,154	8. $654
$2,995	$875	$115	24	9. $3,635	10. $640
$8,229	$1,500	$226	36	11. $9,636	12. $1,407
$4,789	$750	$218	24	13. $5,982	14. $1,193

Solve.

15. With a down payment of $1,000, Kim can buy a $12,000 car by making 36 monthly payments of $336. What is her total cost? What is the finance charge?
$13,096; $1,096
16. With a down payment of $50, Carlos can buy a $489 camera by making 12 monthly payments of $41. What is the total cost of the camera? What is the finance charge?
$542; $53
17. A stereo system costs $1,450. Jake can buy it on credit by putting $300 down and making 24 monthly payments of $64. What is the finance charge?
$386
18. Ramona bought furniture on credit by paying $375 and agreeing to pay the rest in monthly payments of $140 for two years. After 8 payments, she wants to pay the remaining cost. What is the remaining cost?
$2,240
19. Refer to Problem 18. If the furniture store gives Ramona $250 off the total price for paying early, what is the total amount she will pay for the furniture?
$3,485
20. A $4,000 motorcycle is on sale for $600 less. Anna can buy the bike with a down payment of $500 and monthly payments of $148 for two years. How much will she pay for the motorcycle? What is the finance charge?
$4,052; $652

PRACTICE WORKSHEET 3-4

Dividing Whole Numbers

Divide. Check with multiplication.

1. $9)\overline{927}$ = 103
2. $8)\overline{648}$ = 81
3. $6)\overline{624}$ = 104
4. $3)\overline{930}$ = 310

5. $7)\overline{494}$ = 70 R4
6. $2)\overline{626}$ = 313
7. $4)\overline{972}$ = 243
8. $9)\overline{592}$ = 65 R7

9. $20)\overline{400}$ = 20
10. $32)\overline{440}$ = 13 R24
11. $14)\overline{68}$ = 4 R12
12. $31)\overline{63}$ = 2 R1

13. $42)\overline{135}$ = 3 R9
14. $40)\overline{98}$ = 2 R18
15. $28)\overline{776}$ = 27 R20
16. $62)\overline{354}$ = 5 R44

17. $67)\overline{8,143}$ = 121 R36
18. $36)\overline{7,288}$ = 202 R16
19. $41)\overline{3,895}$ = 95
20. $52)\overline{3,652}$ = 70 R12

Solve.

21. If Jenny drives an average of 45 miles an hour, how long does it take her to drive 585 miles?
13 h

22. In 13 days, 2,834 people visit the exhibit. On the average, how many people visit each day?
218 people

PRACTICE WORKSHEET 3-5

Multiplying and Dividing by Powers of 10

Multiply.

1. 14×10 140
2. 27×100 2,700
3. $58 \times 1,000$ 58,000
4. 256×10^1 2,560
5. 361×10^2 36,100
6. $495 \times 1,000$ 495,000
7. 7.6×10 76
8. 5.2×100 520
9. 8.9×10^3 8,900
10. 4.21×10 42.1
11. 3.73×100 373
12. $6.85 \times 1,000$ 6,850

Divide.

13. $8,024 \div 10$ 802.4
14. $6,371 \div 10^2$ 63.71
15. $5,406 \div 1,000$ 5.406
16. $436 \div 10^1$ 43.6
17. $218 \div 100$ 2.18
18. $153 \div 1,000$ 0.153
19. $1.5 \div 10$ 0.15
20. $3.8 \div 100$ 0.038
21. $7.1 \div 10^3$ 0.0071
22. $0.25 \div 10$ 0.025
23. $0.93 \div 100$ 0.0093
24. $0.84 \div 1,000$ 0.00084

Replace each variable with a power of 10 to make a true sentence.

25. $57 \div y = 0.057$ $y = 10^3$
26. $3.522 \times p = 352.2$ $p = 10^2$
27. $93 \div x = 9.3$ $x = 10^1$
28. $64.027 \times q = 640.27$ $q = 10^1$
29. $0.083 \div w = 0.000083$ $w = 10^3$
30. $502.3 \times s = 5,023$ $s = 10^1$
31. $99.94 \times z = 99,940$ $z = 10^3$
32. $0.049 \times t = 4.9$ $t = 10^2$
33. $2 \times r = 200$ $r = 10^2$
34. $7.324 \div y = 0.07324$ $y = 10^2$

PRACTICE WORKSHEET 3-6

Problem Solving Strategy: Look for a Pattern

Solve.

1. Ralph and Ella are playing a game called "Guess My Rule." Ralph has kept track of his guesses and Ella's responses in this table.

Ralph	0	1	2	3	4	5	6
Ella	10	9	8	7	6	5	

Look for a pattern and predict Ella's response for the number 6. Describe this pattern. 4; subtract the guessed number from 10

3. Brad needs to set up a coding system for files in the library using combinations of letters. He has begun this table.

Letters	1	2	3	4	5
Combinations	1	4	9	16	

How many files can Brad code using the letters A, B, C, D, and E? 25 files

4. If the library has 400 items to code, how many letters will the librarian need to use? 20 letters

5. Billie needs to make a tower of soup cans as a display in a grocery store. Each layer of the tower will be in the shape of a rectangle. The length and the width of each layer will be one less than the layer below it.

How many cans will be needed for the fifth layer of the tower? 42 cans

How many cans will be needed for a 10-layer tower? 570 cans

2. Mollie is using the following chart to help her figure prices for tickets.

Tickets	1	2	3	4
Price	$7.50	$12.50	$17.50	$22.50

A customer came in and ordered 10 tickets. How much should Mollie charge for this order? $52.50

1 LETTER	2 LETTERS	3 LETTERS	4 LETTERS
AA	AB BA BB AA	AA BC AB BD AC CB BA CC BB	AA BC DA AB BD DB AC CA DC AD CB DD BA CC BB CD

top layer
second layer
third layer

ANSWER KEY

Name _____ Date _____

PRACTICE WORKSHEET 3-7

Dividing Decimals

Divide.

1. $6\overline{)1.38}$ **0.23** 2. $7\overline{)7.21}$ **1.03** 3. $9\overline{)0.36}$ **0.04** 4. $3\overline{)9.18}$ **3.06**

5. $0.8\overline{)6.4}$ **8** 6. $0.7\overline{)0.63}$ **0.9** 7. $0.3\overline{)27}$ **90** 8. $8\overline{)2}$ **0.25**

9. $14\overline{)0.56}$ **0.04** 10. $8\overline{)32.2}$ **4.025** 11. $5.3\overline{)0.3869}$ **0.073** 12. $0.8\overline{)3.76}$ **4.7**

13. $2.3\overline{)1.61}$ **0.7** 14. $7.8\overline{)0.39}$ **0.05** 15. $4.4\overline{)16.72}$ **3.8** 16. $7.9\overline{)\$41.08}$ **\$5.20**

17. $7.1\overline{)0.0426}$ **0.006** 18. $6.5\overline{)\$769.34}$ **\$118.36** 19. $0.83\overline{)0.1909}$ **0.23** 20. $7.9\overline{)0.1185}$ **0.015**

21. \$0.84 ÷ 12 **\$0.07** 22. 0.414 ÷ 3 **0.138** 23. 25 ÷ 0.5 **50** 24. 139.4 ÷ 4.1 **34**

Solve.

25. How many nickels can Jeb get for \$7.35? **147 nickels**

26. Kara can park her car for 1 hour for 75¢. If she spends \$3.00 on parking, how long does she park? **4 hours**

29

Name _____ Date _____

PRACTICE WORKSHEET 3-8

Scientific Notation

Write in scientific notation.

1. 860 8.6×10^2 2. 2,000 2×10^3 3. 7,200 7.2×10^3
4. 840,000 8.4×10^5 5. 163,000 1.63×10^5 6. 87,400 8.74×10^4
7. 2,340 2.34×10^3 8. 3 million 3×10^6 9. 595,000 5.95×10^5
10. 480 4.8×10^2 11. 14,380 1.438×10^4 12. 6 thousand 6×10^3
13. 2,540 2.54×10^3 14. 13,800 1.38×10^4 15. 352,000 3.52×10^5
16. 156 1.56×10^2 17. 4,230,000 4.23×10^6 18. 37,700 3.77×10^4
19. 5,220,000 5.22×10^6 20. 455,000 4.55×10^5 21. 25,200,000 2.52×10^7
22. 43,200 4.32×10^4 23. 20 billion 2.0×10^{10} 24. 4 million 4×10^6

Write in standard form.

25. 1.9×10^5 **190,000** 26. 3.7×10^3 **3,700** 27. 6.82×10^6 **6,820,000**
28. 1.67×10^3 **1,670** 29. 5.38×10^5 **538,000** 30. 9.73×10^4 **97,300**
31. 4.4×10^9 **4,400,000,000** 32. 2.3×10^8 **230,000,000** 33. 7.85×10^7 **78,500,000**
34. 7.65×10^5 **765,000** 35. 8.79×10^6 **8,790,000** 36. 4.92×10^3 **4,920**
37. 3.19×10^5 **319,000** 38. 1.5×10^9 **1,500,000,000** 39. 7.92×10^3 **7,920**
40. 2.77×10^8 **277,000,000** 41. 2×10^6 **2,000,000** 42. 6.01×10^7 **60,100,000**

30

Name _____ Date _____

PRACTICE LESSON 3-9

Geometric Sequences

Find the common ratio and write the next three terms in each geometric sequence.

1. 6, 18, 54, 162, □, □, □ **3** 486; 1,458; 4,374
2. 14, 28, 56, 112, □, □, □ **2** 224; 448; 896
3. 405, 135, 45, 15, □, □, □ **$\frac{1}{3}$ or** 5, 1.6, 0.5 **0.333**
4. 48, 24, 12, 6, □, □, □ **$\frac{1}{2}$ or 0.5** 3, 1.5, 0.75
5. 3, 15, 75, 375, □, □, □ **5** 1,875; 9,375; 46,875
6. 0.5, 5, 50, 500, □, □, □ **10** 5,000; 50,000; 500,000
7. 3, 6, 12, 24, □, □, □ **5** 48; 96; 192
8. 4, 20, 100, 500, □, □, □ **5** 2,500; 12,500; 62,500
9. 3, 12, 48, 192, □, □, □ **4** 768; 3,072; 12,288
10. 1.4, 2.8, 5.6, 11.2, □, □, □ **2** 22.4; 44.8; 89.6
11. 1.3, 2.6, 5.2, 10.4, □, □, □ **2** 20.8; 41.6; 83.2
12. 800, 200, 50, 12.5, □, □, □ **$\frac{1}{4}$ or 0.25** 3.125; 0.78125; 0.1953125
13. 0.12, 0.48, 1.92, 7.68, □, □, □ **4** 30.72; 122.88; 491.52
14. 5, 5.5, 6.05, 6.655, □, □, □ **1.1** 7.3205; 8.05255; 8.857805
15. 2, 12, 72, 432, □, □, □ **6** 2,592; 15,552; 93,312
16. 2.7, 8.1, 24.3, 72.9, □, □, □ **3** 218.7; 656.1; 1,968.3
17. 2, 3, 4.5, 6.75, □, □, □ **1.5** 10.125; 15.1875; 22.78125
18. 8.8, 4.4, 2.2, 1.1, □, □, □ **0.5** 0.55; 0.275; 0.1375
19. 80.6, 40.3, 20.15, 10.075, □, □, □ **0.5** 5.0375; 2.51875; 1.259375
20. 1.5, 12, 96, 768, □, □, □ **8** 6,144; 49,152; 393,216
21. 0.8, 2, 5, 12.5, □, □, □ **2.5** 31.25; 78.125; 195.3125
22. 900, 450, 225, 112.5, □, □, □ **0.5** 56.25; 28.125; 14.0625

Solve.

23. Inez is playing a video game. The longer she keeps her token active, the higher the point values become, doubling every minute. If the point value at the start was 20, what will the value be if she keeps her token active for 10 minutes? **20,480 points**

24. Water is being lost through a leak in a tank. The hole causing the leak is widening and the water loss has been tripled each day. If 2 gallons were lost on the first day, how many gallons would be lost on the seventh day? **1,458 gallons**

31

Name _____ Date _____

PRACTICE WORKSHEET 3-10

Formulas

A formula for finding the amount of work needed is W = Fd. Find the amount of work needed.

1. F= 12 lb; d = 20 ft **240 ft-lb** 2. F= 28 lb; d = 150 ft **4,200 ft-lb**
3. F= 90 lb; d = 25 ft **2,250 ft-lb** 4. F= 175 lb; d = 20.5 ft **3,587.5 ft-lb**
5. F= 99 lb; d = 5.5 ft **544.5 ft-lb** 6. F= 150 lb; d = 50 ft **7,500 ft-lb**

Find the circumference of each circle. Use 3.14 for π.

7. d = 33 cm **103.62 cm** 8. r = 26 ft **163.28 ft**
9. d = 4.2 in. **26.376 in.** 10. d = 7.5 m **23.55 m**

A formula for determining a normal blood pressure reading (B.P.) is B.P. = $110 + \frac{A}{2}$. The A stands for age in years. Find the normal blood pressure for each age.

15. 16 **118** 16. 78 **149** 17. 21 **120.5** 18. 35 **127.5**
19. 56 **138** 20. 65 **142.5** 21. 37 **128.5** 22. 75 **147.5**

Write a formula. Then solve.

23. The air distance from Boston, Massachusetts to San Francisco, California is about 2,700 mi. If a flight from Boston to San Francisco takes 6 h, at what rate does the plane fly? **r = 2,700 ÷ 6, 450 mph**

24. The road distance from Boston to San Francisco is about 3,200 mi. To the nearest hundredth, how many hours of driving time will it take Ms. Costello if her rate is 55 mph? **h = 3,200 ÷ 55, 58.18 h**

25. Ms. Costello's car averages 28 miles per gallon of gasoline. To the nearest hundredth, how many gallons will be used for the drive from Boston to San Francisco? **g = 3,200 ÷ 28, 114.29 gal**

26. If gasoline on average costs \$1.35 per gallon, to the nearest cent how much will Ms. Costello spend on gasoline for the drive from Boston to San Francisco? **c = \$1.35 x 114.29, \$154.29**

32

ANSWER KEY

Name _____ Date _____

PRACTICE WORKSHEET 3-11

Area of Rectangles

Find the area of each rectangle.

1. **48 ft²** (4 ft, 12 ft)
2. **243 in²** (9 in., 27 in.)
3. **1.5 ft² = 216 in²** (3 ft, 6 in.)
4. **450 m²** (75 m, 6 m)
5. **5,796 cm²** (63 cm, 92 cm)
6. **9,350 mm² = 93.5 cm²** (8.5 cm, 110 mm)

7. length, 37 km; width, 12 km
   444 km²
8. length, 5 in.; width, 3.5 in.
   17.5 in²
9. length, 38 in.; width, 2 ft
   912 in² = 6⅓ ft²
10. length, 18 in.; width, 6 cm
    108 cm²
11. length, 9 cm; width, 3.5 cm
    31.5 cm²
12. length, 41 feet; width, 75 feet
    3,075 ft²
13. length, 18 in.; width, 2 yd
    1,296 in² = 1 yd²
14. length, 2 km; width, 0.075 km
    0.15 km²

Solve.

15. A family room floor measures 18 feet 6 inches by 15 feet 3 inches. Find the area of the floor in square feet.
    281.125 ft²
16. An expert painter with a sprayer can cover about 600 square feet of wall surface in half an hour. How long would it take an expert to paint both sides of a corridor in which each wall is 10 feet high by 90 feet long?
    1.5 hours
17. Plastic sheeting is sold in rolls that are 30 inches wide. The strip of sheeting on a roll is 75 yards long. How many square feet of sheeting are on a roll?
    562.5 ft²
18. José can cut 10,000 square feet of grass in an hour. How long would it take him to cut a rectangular yard that measures 50 yards by 100 yards?
    4.5 hours

Name _____ Date _____

PRACTICE WORKSHEET 3-12

Statistics: Average (Mean)

Find the mean for each set of data. Round to the nearest tenth or cent.

1. 10, 10, 15, 10, 4, 1, 15
   9.3
2. 59, 69, 73, 74, 61, 67, 59, 58
   65
3. $175, $176, $172, $177, $177, $175, $175, $176, $176, $177, $173
   $175.36
4. 75, 80, 73, 74, 80, 80, 76, 74, 67, 70
   74.9
5. 1.4, 1.5, 1.4, 1.44, 1.39, 1.48, 1.47, 1.49, 1.49, 1.42, 1.42, 1.40
   1.4
6. 144, 143, 143, 138, 137, 146, 135, 141, 135, 147, 138, 134
   140.1
7. 0.65, 1.62, 0.63, 1.66, 0.62, 0.65, 1.66, 0.64, 0.62, 1.62, 0.65
   1.0
8. $1.60, $1.56, $1.60, $1.63, $1.59, $1.60, $1.63, $1.61, $1.58, $1.60
   $1.60

Solve.

9. In the first five basketball games of the season, Jojo scored 12, 15, 22, 9, and 18 points. What was Jojo's average for these five games?
   15.2
10. Millen went bowling with her friends. Her scores were 182, 151, 127, and 167. What was Millen's average for these four games?
    156.75

Name _____ Date _____

PRACTICE WORKSHEET 3-13

Problem Solving: Multi-Step Problems

Solve.

1. Roy receives $45 for his birthday. He buys a new book for $7.98, a shirt for $13.99, and a puzzle game for $4.59. How much does he have left to put in his savings account?
   $18.44
2. Connie earns money painting house numbers on curbs. In three weeks, she earns $175, $145, and $130. She pays a supply bill of $81.30. How much does she have left?
   $368.70
3. Earl, Steve, and Don walk dogs for their summer spending money. They walk 5 dogs for 8 weeks and are paid $6 per week for each dog. What is each boy's share if they divide the money evenly?
   $80.00
4. Pat earned $22.75. Her parents gave her $20. How much more does she need to buy a sweater that costs $50?
   $7.25
5. Luis earns $45 each week. He saves $12.75 each week. In how many weeks will he have enough money to buy a CD player that costs $135?
   11 weeks
6. Duwayne's lunch cost $5.35. He had a sandwich for $2.95, a drink for $0.89, and dessert. How much did dessert cost?
   $1.51
7. Mara works at a restaurant. She makes $3.75 an hour. She worked 20 hours and made $104.50 in tips. How much did she earn?
   $179.50
8. Crystal bought 2 shirts for $19.95 each and 3 pairs of socks at $3.89 a pair. Tax is $3.49. She gives the clerk three twenty-dollar bills. What is her change?
   $4.94

Use the passbook to find the balance on each of the following dates.

9. Sept. 15   10. Oct. 31
   $118.10   **$139.67**
11. How much must Robin save to have $150?
    $10.33

Name _____ Date _____

PRACTICE WORKSHEET 4-1

Factors and Divisibility

Find all the factors of each number.

1. 8   **1, 2, 4, 8**
2. 15   **1, 3, 5, 15**
3. 21   **1, 3, 7, 21**
4. 27   **1, 3, 9, 27**
5. 33   **1, 3, 11, 33**
6. 36   **1, 2, 3, 4, 6, 9, 12, 18, 36**
7. 42   **1, 2, 3, 6, 7, 14, 21, 42**
8. 48   **1, 2, 3, 4, 6, 8, 12, 16, 24, 48**
9. 50   **1, 2, 5, 10, 25, 50**
10. 54   **1, 2, 3, 6, 9, 18, 27, 54**

State whether each number is divisible by 2, 3, 5, 9, or 10.

11. 110   **2, 5, 10**
12. 225   **3, 5, 9**
13. 315   **3, 5, 9**
14. 405   **3, 5, 9**
15. 918   **2, 3, 9**
16. 243   **3, 9**
17. 630   **2, 3, 5, 9, 10**
18. 735   **3, 5**
19. 1,233   **3, 9**
20. 2,460   **2, 3, 5, 10**
21. 5,103   **3, 9**
22. 8,001   **3, 9**
23. 9,270   **2, 3, 5, 9, 10**
24. 44,127   **3, 9**
25. 117,930   **2, 3, 5, 10**

ANSWER KEY

Name _____ Date _____

PRACTICE WORKSHEET 4-2

Prime Factorization

Write the prime factorization of each number.

1. 24

2. 78

3. 625
5×125
$5 \times 5 \times 25$
$5 \times 5 \times 5 \times 5$

Make factor trees to express the prime factorization of each of the following. Write the prime factorization of each number.

4. 18
2×9
$2 \times 3 \times 3$
2×3^2

5. 42
2×21
$2 \times 3 \times 7$
$2 \times 3 \times 7$

6. 144 $2^4 \times 3^2$
2×72
$2 \times 2 \times 36$
$2 \times 2 \times 2 \times 18$
$2 \times 2 \times 2 \times 2 \times 9$
$2 \times 2 \times 2 \times 2 \times 3 \times 3$

Write the prime factorization of each number.

7. 8 2^3
8. 25 5^2
9. 81 3^4
10. 100 $2^2 \times 5^2$
11. 250 2×5^3
12. 324 $2^2 \times 3^4$
13. 72 $2^3 \times 3^2$
14. 156 $2^2 \times 3 \times 13$
15. 111 3×37
16. 128 2^7
17. 625 5^4
18. 550 $2 \times 5^2 \times 11$
19. 405 $3^4 \times 5$
20. 243 3^5
21. 500 $2^2 \times 5^3$
22. 512 2^9

Complete the following.

23. List the prime numbers less than 30. 2, 3, 5, 7, 11, 13, 17, 19, 23, 29

24. What is the least prime factor of 221? 13

Name _____ Date _____

PRACTICE WORKSHEET 4-3

Greatest Common Factor and Least Common Multiple

Find the GCF of each group of numbers.

1. 12 1, 2, 3, 4, 6, 12, or $2 \times 2 \times 3$
   27 1, 3, 9, 27, or $3 \times 3 \times 3$
   GCF: 3

2. 25 1, 5, 25, or 5×5
   30 1, 2, 3, 5, 6, 10, 15, 30 or $2 \times 3 \times 5$
   GCF: 5

3. 16 1, 2, 4, 8, 16 or $2 \times 2 \times 2 \times 2$
   24 1, 2, 3, 4, 6, 8, 12, 24 or $2 \times 2 \times 2 \times 3$
   GCF: 8

4. 48 1, 2, 3, 4, 6, 8, 12, 16, 24, 48 or $2 \times 2 \times 2 \times 2 \times 3$
   60 1, 2, 3, 4, 5, 6, 10, 12, 15, 20, 30, 60 or $2 \times 2 \times 3 \times 5$
   GCF: 12

5. 60 1, 2, 3, 4, 5, 6, 10, 12, 15, 20, 30, 60 or $2 \times 2 \times 3 \times 5$
   75 1, 3, 5, 15, 25, 75 or $3 \times 5 \times 5$
   GCF: 15

6. 54 1, 2, 3, 6, 9, 18, 27, 54 or $2 \times 3 \times 3 \times 3$
   72 1, 2, 3, 4, 6, 8, 9, 12, 18, 24, 36, 72 or $2 \times 2 \times 2 \times 3 \times 3$
   GCF: 18

Find the LCM of each group of numbers.

7. 6 0, 6, 12, 18, 24, 30, . . . or 2×3
   30 0, 30, 60, . . . or $2 \times 3 \times 5$
   LCM: 30

8. 30 0, 30, 60, . . . or $2 \times 3 \times 5$
   10 0, 10, 20, 30, 40, . . . or 2×5
   LCM: 30

9. 12 0, 12, 24, 36, 48, 60, 72, 84, . . . or $2 \times 2 \times 3$
   42 0, 42, 84, . . . or $2 \times 3 \times 7$
   LCM: 84

10. 12 0, 12, 24, 36, 48, . . . or $2 \times 2 \times 3$
    18 0, 18, 36, 54, . . . or $2 \times 3 \times 3$
    LCM: 36

11. 8 0, 8, 16, 24, 32, 40, . . . or $2 \times 2 \times 2$
    10 0, 10, 20, 30, 40, 50, . . . or 2×5
    LCM: 40

12. 15 0, 15, 30, 45, 60, 75, . . . or 3×5
    75 0, 75, 150, . . . or $3 \times 5 \times 5$
    LCM: 75

Name _____ Date _____

PRACTICE WORKSHEET 4-4

Applications: Total Deductions and Take-Home Pay

Complete the chart.

	Name	Gross Pay	Total Tax Deduction	Total Personal Deduction	Take-Home Pay
1.	S. Cook	$247.80	$37.17	$35.00	$175.63
2.	R. Choi	$215.62	$29.48	$8.75	$177.39
3.	T. Brady	$195.75	$27.16	$20.00	$148.59
4.	L. Sanchez	$228.30	$32.53	$9.95	$185.82
5.	F. Hyde	$239.44	$35.46	$15.50	$188.48
6.	P. Morgan	$175.25	$23.92	$7.25	$144.08
7.	N. Hill	$188.50	$24.18	$9.40	$154.92
8.	D. Tallchief	$203.22	$25.81	$18.75	$158.66
9.	R. Sanders	$217.95	$29.76	$24.00	$164.19
10.	J. Ortega	$224.50	$31.27	$17.50	$175.73
11.	L. Horton	$206.74	$27.44	$9.36	$169.94
12.	A. Cheng	$185.75	$22.19	$5.00	$158.56
13.	T. McVay	$200.50	$24.52	$8.25	$167.73
14.	S. Shelton	$236.40	$38.73	$25.00	$172.67
15.	M. Jordan	$242.83	$36.84	$18.50	$187.49

Name _____ Date _____

PRACTICE WORKSHEET 4-5

Equivalent Fractions

Replace each ☐ with a number so that the fractions are equivalent.

1. $\frac{2}{3} = \frac{4}{6}$
2. $\frac{3}{16} = \frac{9}{48}$
3. $\frac{1}{3} = \frac{4}{12}$
4. $\frac{6}{7} = \frac{42}{49}$
5. $\frac{15}{20} = \frac{3}{4}$
6. $\frac{4}{12} = \frac{1}{3}$
7. $\frac{4}{16} = \frac{1}{4}$
8. $\frac{5}{10} = \frac{1}{2}$
9. $\frac{3}{4} = \frac{9}{12}$
10. $\frac{3}{4} = \frac{6}{8}$
11. $\frac{1}{3} = \frac{2}{6}$
12. $\frac{1}{2} = \frac{3}{6}$
13. $\frac{7}{7} = \frac{1}{1}$
14. $\frac{3}{7} = \frac{18}{42}$
15. $\frac{3}{15} = \frac{1}{5}$
16. $\frac{4}{32} = \frac{1}{8}$
17. $\frac{1}{25} = \frac{4}{100}$
18. $\frac{7}{18} = \frac{14}{36}$
19. $\frac{0}{3} = \frac{0}{36}$
20. $\frac{6}{18} = \frac{1}{3}$
21. $\frac{1}{3} = \frac{5}{15}$
22. $\frac{3}{7} = \frac{9}{21}$
23. $\frac{2}{5} = \frac{10}{25}$
24. $\frac{3}{10} = \frac{30}{100}$

Name a fraction equivalent to each fraction.

25. $\frac{1}{3}$ $\frac{2}{6}$
26. $\frac{1}{2}$ $\frac{5}{10}$
27. $\frac{1}{4}$ $\frac{2}{8}$
28. $\frac{3}{6}$ $\frac{1}{2}$
29. $\frac{5}{8}$ $\frac{10}{16}$
30. $\frac{44}{48}$ $\frac{11}{12}$

Answers may vary. Sample answers are given.

31. Write three fractions that are equivalent to $\frac{6}{10}$.
   $\frac{12}{20}, \frac{18}{30}, \frac{24}{40}$

32. Name three fractions that are equivalent to $\frac{35}{100}$.
   $\frac{7}{20}, \frac{14}{40}, \frac{21}{60}$

Answers may vary. Sample answers are given.

ANSWER KEY

Name _____ Date _____

PRACTICE WORKSHEET 4-6

Simplifying Fractions
Simplify.

1. $\frac{5}{10}$ $\frac{1}{2}$
2. $\frac{4}{10}$ $\frac{2}{5}$
3. $\frac{9}{12}$ $\frac{3}{4}$
4. $\frac{18}{24}$ $\frac{3}{4}$

5. $\frac{9}{24}$ $\frac{3}{8}$
6. $\frac{16}{20}$ $\frac{4}{5}$
7. $\frac{13}{39}$ $\frac{1}{3}$
8. $\frac{16}{48}$ $\frac{1}{3}$

9. $\frac{8}{16}$ $\frac{1}{2}$
10. $\frac{9}{12}$ $\frac{3}{4}$
11. $\frac{15}{18}$ $\frac{5}{6}$
12. $\frac{5}{35}$ $\frac{1}{7}$

13. $\frac{20}{24}$ $\frac{5}{6}$
14. $\frac{14}{16}$ $\frac{7}{8}$
15. $\frac{16}{18}$ $\frac{8}{9}$
16. $\frac{9}{15}$ $\frac{3}{5}$

17. $\frac{7}{21}$ $\frac{1}{3}$
18. $\frac{6}{16}$ $\frac{3}{8}$
19. $\frac{20}{36}$ $\frac{5}{9}$
20. $\frac{33}{39}$ $\frac{11}{13}$

21. $\frac{18}{24}$ $\frac{3}{4}$
22. $\frac{24}{36}$ $\frac{2}{3}$
23. $\frac{32}{48}$ $\frac{2}{3}$
24. $\frac{66}{121}$ $\frac{6}{11}$

25. $\frac{17}{34}$ $\frac{1}{2}$
26. $\frac{4}{40}$ $\frac{1}{10}$
27. $\frac{26}{39}$ $\frac{2}{3}$
28. $\frac{20}{50}$ $\frac{2}{5}$

29. $\frac{25}{75}$ $\frac{1}{3}$
30. $\frac{32}{80}$ $\frac{2}{5}$
31. $\frac{60}{72}$ $\frac{5}{6}$
32. $\frac{30}{45}$ $\frac{2}{3}$

Member	Tickets sold
Ryko	73
Paul	80
Amy	75
Miguel	50
Yvonne	92
Jerome	70

Solve. Use the chart.

33. Rank the members from 1 through 6. The one who sold the most tickets gets a rank of 1.

34. Each member had 100 tickets to sell. Write each member's sale as a fraction in simplest form.

1. Yvonne - $\frac{23}{25}$
2. Paul - $\frac{4}{5}$
3. Amy - $\frac{3}{4}$
4. Ryko - $\frac{73}{100}$
5. Jerome - $\frac{7}{10}$
6. Miguel - $\frac{1}{2}$

Glencoe Division, Macmillan/McGraw-Hill

41

Name _____ Date _____

PRACTICE WORKSHEET 4-7

Comparing Fractions
Write >, <, or = in each circle to make a true sentence.

1. $\frac{1}{3}$ < $\frac{3}{4}$
2. $\frac{3}{8}$ > $\frac{1}{8}$
3. $\frac{5}{6}$ > $\frac{3}{7}$

4. $\frac{1}{2}$ > $\frac{2}{7}$
5. $\frac{16}{20}$ = $\frac{4}{5}$
6. $\frac{3}{4}$ > $\frac{2}{7}$

7. $\frac{3}{5}$ < $\frac{4}{5}$
8. $\frac{2}{3}$ > $\frac{2}{5}$
9. $\frac{1}{3}$ < $\frac{5}{7}$

10. $\frac{2}{7}$ < $\frac{4}{7}$
11. $\frac{3}{16}$ > $\frac{1}{8}$
12. $\frac{1}{4}$ < $\frac{3}{4}$

13. $\frac{1}{6}$ > $\frac{1}{7}$
14. $\frac{5}{9}$ < $\frac{2}{3}$
15. $\frac{2}{11}$ = $\frac{6}{33}$

16. $\frac{3}{5}$ > $\frac{3}{8}$
17. $\frac{2}{7}$ < $\frac{2}{5}$
18. $\frac{3}{9}$ = $\frac{15}{45}$

19. $\frac{3}{5}$ < $\frac{2}{3}$
20. $\frac{4}{9}$ > $\frac{2}{5}$
21. $\frac{4}{5}$ > $\frac{7}{10}$

22. $\frac{3}{4}$ > $\frac{3}{5}$
23. $\frac{1}{3}$ > $\frac{1}{4}$
24. $\frac{1}{4}$ > $\frac{1}{5}$

25. $\frac{5}{6}$ < $\frac{6}{7}$
26. $\frac{5}{6}$ > $\frac{4}{7}$
27. $\frac{7}{8}$ < $\frac{9}{10}$

28. $\frac{2}{3}$ < $\frac{5}{6}$
29. $\frac{9}{10}$ < $\frac{11}{12}$
30. $\frac{3}{10}$ < $\frac{1}{3}$

Order the following fractions from least to greatest.

31. $\frac{2}{3}, \frac{3}{4}, \frac{1}{2}, \frac{1}{8}$ $\frac{1}{8}, \frac{1}{2}, \frac{2}{3}, \frac{3}{4}$
32. $\frac{1}{3}, \frac{1}{6}, \frac{1}{9}, \frac{1}{2}$ $\frac{1}{9}, \frac{1}{6}, \frac{1}{3}, \frac{1}{2}$
33. $\frac{5}{6}, \frac{2}{3}, \frac{3}{4}, \frac{7}{12}$ $\frac{7}{12}, \frac{2}{3}, \frac{3}{4}, \frac{5}{6}$
34. $\frac{2}{5}, \frac{3}{10}, \frac{1}{4}, \frac{3}{20}$ $\frac{3}{20}, \frac{1}{4}, \frac{3}{10}, \frac{2}{5}$

Glencoe Division, Macmillan/McGraw-Hill

42

Name _____ Date _____

PRACTICE WORKSHEET 4-8

Mixed Numbers
Change each fraction to a mixed number in simplest form.

1. $\frac{9}{5}$ $1\frac{4}{5}$
2. $\frac{7}{6}$ $1\frac{1}{6}$
3. $\frac{19}{12}$ $1\frac{7}{12}$
4. $\frac{14}{10}$ $1\frac{2}{5}$

5. $\frac{15}{9}$ $1\frac{2}{3}$
6. $\frac{7}{2}$ $3\frac{1}{2}$
7. $\frac{3}{2}$ $1\frac{1}{2}$
8. $\frac{5}{4}$ $1\frac{1}{4}$

9. $\frac{9}{7}$ $1\frac{2}{7}$
10. $\frac{9}{2}$ $4\frac{1}{2}$
11. $\frac{11}{4}$ $2\frac{3}{4}$
12. $\frac{12}{5}$ $2\frac{2}{5}$

13. $\frac{6}{4}$ $1\frac{1}{2}$
14. $\frac{9}{6}$ $1\frac{1}{2}$
15. $\frac{21}{15}$ $1\frac{2}{5}$
16. $\frac{55}{16}$ $3\frac{7}{16}$

17. $\frac{16}{3}$ $5\frac{1}{3}$
18. $\frac{14}{5}$ $2\frac{4}{5}$
19. $\frac{24}{20}$ $1\frac{1}{5}$
20. $\frac{22}{6}$ $3\frac{2}{3}$

Change each mixed number to an improper fraction.

21. $3\frac{1}{16}$ $\frac{49}{16}$
22. $2\frac{3}{4}$ $\frac{11}{4}$
23. $1\frac{3}{8}$ $\frac{11}{8}$
24. $1\frac{5}{12}$ $\frac{17}{12}$

25. $7\frac{3}{5}$ $\frac{38}{5}$
26. $6\frac{5}{8}$ $\frac{53}{8}$
27. $3\frac{1}{3}$ $\frac{10}{3}$
28. $1\frac{7}{9}$ $\frac{16}{9}$

29. $2\frac{3}{16}$ $\frac{35}{16}$
30. $1\frac{2}{3}$ $\frac{5}{3}$
31. $3\frac{3}{10}$ $\frac{33}{10}$
32. $4\frac{3}{25}$ $\frac{103}{25}$

33. $4\frac{2}{5}$ $\frac{22}{5}$
34. $6\frac{1}{2}$ $\frac{13}{2}$
35. $4\frac{5}{6}$ $\frac{29}{6}$
36. $1\frac{1}{100}$ $\frac{101}{100}$

37. $2\frac{5}{8}$ $\frac{21}{8}$
38. $3\frac{1}{6}$ $\frac{19}{6}$
39. $4\frac{3}{5}$ $\frac{23}{5}$
40. $1\frac{49}{50}$ $\frac{99}{50}$

Solve.

41. How many pounds of margarine does Joel have if he has seven quarter-pound sticks?

$1\frac{3}{4}$ **pounds**

42. How many quarters did Nancy play if she played in $2\frac{3}{4}$ basketball games?

11 quarters

Glencoe Division, Macmillan/McGraw-Hill

43

Name _____ Date _____

PRACTICE WORKSHEET 4-9

Estimating Sums and Differences
Estimate.

Answers may vary. Typical answers are given.

1. $\frac{7}{16} + \frac{2}{9}$ $\frac{1}{2}$
2. $\frac{5}{6} + \frac{1}{3}$ 1

3. $\frac{1}{4} - \frac{1}{3}$ 0
4. $\frac{2}{15} + 2\frac{1}{20}$ 2

5. $\frac{24}{25} - \frac{1}{2}$ $\frac{1}{2}$
6. $1\frac{1}{3} + \frac{2}{5}$ $1\frac{1}{2}$

7. $\frac{4}{5} - \frac{1}{8}$ 1
8. $\frac{5}{8} + \frac{4}{9}$ 1

9. $3\frac{2}{5} - 1\frac{1}{4}$ $2\frac{1}{2}$
10. $\frac{11}{12} - \frac{1}{3}$ 1

11. $4\frac{2}{5} + \frac{5}{6}$ $5\frac{1}{2}$
12. $6\frac{7}{8} - \frac{2}{3}$ 6

13. $4\frac{7}{12} - 1\frac{3}{4}$ $2\frac{1}{2}$
14. $9\frac{7}{10} + \frac{4}{5}$ $10\frac{1}{2}$

15. $4\frac{2}{3} + 10\frac{3}{8}$ $15\frac{1}{2}$
16. $18\frac{1}{4} - 12\frac{3}{5}$ $5\frac{1}{2}$

17. $7\frac{7}{15} - 3\frac{1}{12}$ $4\frac{1}{2}$
18. $12\frac{5}{9} + 8\frac{5}{8}$ 21

Glencoe Division, Macmillan/McGraw-Hill

44

157
Glencoe Division, Macmillan/McGraw-Hill

ANSWER KEY

Name _____ Date _____

PRACTICE WORKSHEET 4-10

Adding Fractions

Add.

1. $\frac{4}{7} + \frac{2}{7}$ $\frac{6}{7}$
2. $\frac{6}{9} + \frac{3}{9}$ 1
3. $\frac{11}{15} + \frac{2}{15}$ $\frac{13}{15}$

4. $\frac{11}{15} + \frac{7}{15}$ $1\frac{1}{5}$
5. $\frac{15}{20} + \frac{7}{20}$ $1\frac{1}{10}$
6. $\frac{9}{11} + \frac{8}{11}$ $1\frac{6}{11}$

7. $\frac{12}{20} + \frac{7}{20}$ $\frac{19}{20}$
8. $\frac{1}{5} + \frac{1}{4}$ $\frac{9}{20}$
9. $\frac{6}{7} + \frac{6}{7}$ $1\frac{5}{7}$

10. $\frac{7}{10} + \frac{3}{5}$ $1\frac{3}{10}$
11. $\frac{5}{8} + \frac{1}{4}$ $\frac{7}{8}$
12. $\frac{8}{15} + \frac{2}{3}$ $1\frac{1}{5}$

13. $\frac{5}{12} + \frac{1}{3}$ $\frac{3}{4}$
14. $\frac{2}{3} + \frac{1}{6}$ $\frac{5}{6}$
15. $\frac{5}{6} + \frac{5}{18}$ $1\frac{1}{9}$

16. $\frac{3}{5} + \frac{2}{3}$ $1\frac{4}{15}$
17. $\frac{1}{2} + \frac{3}{7}$ $\frac{13}{14}$
18. $\frac{1}{2} + \frac{3}{8}$ $\frac{7}{8}$

19. $\frac{1}{6} + \frac{3}{5}$ $\frac{23}{30}$
20. $\frac{7}{8} + \frac{5}{6}$ $1\frac{17}{24}$
21. $\frac{1}{12} + \frac{2}{5}$ $\frac{29}{60}$

22. $\frac{1}{8} + \frac{5}{6} + \frac{7}{12}$ $1\frac{13}{24}$
23. $\frac{1}{2} + \frac{2}{3} + \frac{1}{6}$ $1\frac{1}{3}$

Solve.

24. Paul earns $48.24 each week. He saves $\frac{1}{4}$ of his earnings and spends $\frac{2}{3}$ on clothes and school supplies. What fraction of his earnings does he set aside for savings, clothes, and school supplies? $\frac{11}{12}$

25. In the 8th grade, $\frac{11}{25}$ of the students wear watches. In the 9th grade, $\frac{3}{5}$ of the students wear watches. In which grade do more students wear watches?   **9th grade**

45

Glencoe Division, Macmillan/McGraw-Hill

Name _____ Date _____

PRACTICE WORKSHEET 4-11

Adding Mixed Numbers

Add.

1. $2\frac{1}{8}$
   $+ 3\frac{3}{8}$
   $5\frac{1}{2}$
2. $5\frac{5}{6}$
   $+ 8\frac{1}{6}$
   14
3. $7\frac{3}{4}$
   $+ 1\frac{2}{4}$
   $9\frac{1}{4}$
4. $8\frac{3}{8}$
   $+ 2\frac{7}{8}$
   $11\frac{1}{4}$

5. $5\frac{3}{8}$
   $+ 4\frac{1}{4}$
   $9\frac{5}{8}$
6. $7\frac{3}{5}$
   $+ 2\frac{1}{3}$
   $9\frac{14}{15}$
7. $4\frac{1}{2}$
   $+ 10\frac{3}{7}$
   $14\frac{13}{14}$
8. $9\frac{5}{6}$
   $+ 7\frac{2}{9}$
   $17\frac{1}{18}$

9. $6\frac{3}{5}$
   $+ 3\frac{1}{4}$
   $9\frac{17}{20}$
10. $8\frac{2}{3}$
    $+ 4\frac{5}{7}$
    $13\frac{8}{21}$
11. $5\frac{1}{6}$
    $+ 6\frac{6}{7}$
    $12\frac{1}{42}$
12. $3\frac{5}{8}$
    $+ 7\frac{1}{3}$
    $10\frac{23}{24}$

13. $3\frac{1}{9} + 5\frac{5}{6}$ 9
14. $12\frac{5}{9} + 7\frac{5}{9}$ $20\frac{1}{9}$
15. $2\frac{1}{8} + 1\frac{2}{5}$ $3\frac{29}{40}$

16. $6\frac{3}{5} + 3\frac{1}{6}$ $9\frac{23}{30}$
17. $3\frac{4}{5} + 1\frac{9}{10}$ $5\frac{7}{10}$
18. $12\frac{11}{12} + 9\frac{2}{3}$ $22\frac{7}{12}$

19. $9\frac{7}{8} + 8\frac{5}{6}$ $18\frac{17}{24}$
20. $14\frac{7}{20} + 6\frac{4}{5}$ $21\frac{3}{20}$
21. $2\frac{1}{4} + 1\frac{1}{2}$ $3\frac{3}{4}$

22. $22\frac{7}{8} + 7\frac{1}{6}$ $30\frac{1}{24}$
23. $15\frac{1}{2} + 4\frac{3}{4}$ $20\frac{1}{4}$
24. $12\frac{4}{5} + 8\frac{5}{6}$ $21\frac{19}{30}$

25. $4\frac{1}{12} + 3\frac{5}{12} + 5\frac{7}{12}$ $13\frac{1}{12}$
26. $2\frac{1}{2} + 1\frac{1}{4} + \frac{1}{8}$ $3\frac{7}{8}$

27. $2\frac{4}{9} + 3\frac{2}{3} + 1\frac{1}{6}$ $7\frac{5}{18}$
28. $4\frac{5}{12} + 1\frac{3}{8} + 1\frac{5}{6}$ $7\frac{5}{8}$

46

Glencoe Division, Macmillan/McGraw-Hill

Name _____ Date _____

PRACTICE WORKSHEET 4-12

Subtracting Fractions

Subtract.

1. $\frac{13}{20} - \frac{7}{20}$ $\frac{3}{10}$
2. $\frac{7}{12} - \frac{5}{12}$ $\frac{1}{6}$
3. $\frac{9}{10} - \frac{7}{10}$ $\frac{1}{5}$

4. $\frac{1}{2} - \frac{1}{3}$ $\frac{1}{6}$
5. $\frac{7}{8} - \frac{5}{6}$ $\frac{1}{24}$
6. $\frac{13}{16} - \frac{7}{12}$ $\frac{11}{48}$

7. $\frac{7}{8} - \frac{7}{12}$ $\frac{7}{24}$
8. $\frac{7}{9} - \frac{3}{5}$ $\frac{8}{45}$
9. $\frac{3}{4} - \frac{13}{20}$ $\frac{1}{10}$

10. $\frac{7}{8} - \frac{2}{3}$ $\frac{5}{24}$
11. $\frac{3}{4} - \frac{2}{3}$ $\frac{1}{12}$
12. $\frac{5}{6} - \frac{5}{8}$ $\frac{5}{24}$

13. $\frac{3}{4} - \frac{1}{2}$ $\frac{1}{4}$
14. $\frac{5}{8} - \frac{9}{16}$ $\frac{1}{16}$
15. $\frac{11}{12} - \frac{1}{8}$ $\frac{19}{24}$

16. $\frac{1}{2} - \frac{1}{8}$ $\frac{3}{8}$
17. $\frac{11}{12} - \frac{1}{4}$ $\frac{2}{3}$
18. $\frac{3}{4} - \frac{1}{8}$ $\frac{5}{8}$

19. $\frac{8}{15} - \frac{1}{6}$ $\frac{11}{30}$
20. $\frac{3}{10} - \frac{1}{5}$ $\frac{1}{10}$
21. $\frac{5}{6} - \frac{7}{9}$ $\frac{1}{18}$

22. $\frac{19}{27} - \frac{10}{27}$ $\frac{1}{3}$
23. $\frac{11}{20} - \frac{2}{5}$ $\frac{3}{20}$
24. $\frac{3}{4} - \frac{5}{12}$ $\frac{1}{3}$

Solve.

25. Mrs. Smith has $\frac{3}{4}$ gallon of milk. She uses $\frac{1}{2}$ gallon. How much does she have left? $\frac{1}{4}$ **gallon**

26. Mr. Morales has 11 eggs. He uses $\frac{1}{4}$ dozen. How many dozen eggs does he have left? $\frac{2}{3}$ **dozen**

47

Glencoe Division, Macmillan/McGraw-Hill

Name _____ Date _____

PRACTICE WORKSHEET 4-13

Subtracting Mixed Numbers

Subtract.

1. $7\frac{3}{4}$
   $- 6\frac{1}{4}$
   $1\frac{1}{2}$
2. $9\frac{7}{8}$
   $- 2\frac{3}{8}$
   $7\frac{1}{2}$
3. 8
   $- 6\frac{1}{5}$
   $1\frac{4}{5}$
4. $10\frac{7}{12}$
   $- 6$
   $4\frac{7}{12}$

5. $2\frac{1}{8}$
   $- 1\frac{1}{16}$
   $1\frac{1}{16}$
6. $12\frac{4}{5}$
   $- 9\frac{3}{10}$
   $3\frac{1}{2}$
7. $6\frac{2}{3}$
   $- 4\frac{1}{4}$
   $2\frac{5}{12}$
8. $7\frac{5}{6}$
   $- 1\frac{3}{4}$
   $6\frac{1}{12}$

9. $7\frac{1}{2}$
   $- 3\frac{3}{4}$
   $3\frac{3}{4}$
10. $4\frac{7}{12}$
    $- 2\frac{2}{3}$
    $1\frac{11}{12}$
11. $6\frac{2}{5}$
    $- 3\frac{1}{2}$
    $2\frac{9}{10}$
12. $11\frac{1}{5}$
    $- 7\frac{1}{3}$
    $3\frac{13}{15}$

13. $5\frac{11}{12} - 2\frac{1}{6}$ $3\frac{3}{4}$
14. $8 - 7\frac{4}{15}$ $\frac{11}{15}$
15. $5\frac{6}{7} - 5\frac{1}{2}$ $\frac{5}{14}$

16. $18\frac{1}{6} - 7\frac{7}{9}$ $10\frac{7}{18}$
17. $16\frac{9}{10} - 8\frac{3}{10}$ $8\frac{3}{5}$
18. $14\frac{1}{7} - 8\frac{4}{7}$ $5\frac{4}{7}$

Solve.

19. After the stock rose $2\frac{3}{8}$ points, it closed at $28\frac{1}{4}$. What was the opening price? $25\frac{7}{8}$

20. Sue and Jerry are making muffins for breakfast. They need $2\frac{1}{2}$ cups of flour, but they have only $1\frac{3}{4}$ cups. How much more flour do they need? $\frac{3}{4}$ cup

48

Glencoe Division, Macmillan/McGraw-Hill

158

Glencoe Division, Macmillan/McGraw-Hill

ANSWER KEY

Name _____ **Date** _____

PRACTICE WORKSHEET 4-14

Problem-Solving Strategy: Make a Drawing

Solve. **Drawings may vary.**

1. A loaf of bread is 10 inches long. How many cuts are necessary to cut it into 12 equal slices?

11 cuts

2. A floor is $6\frac{2}{3}$ feet long and $5\frac{3}{4}$ feet wide. How many 1-foot square tiles are needed to cover the floor?

$5\frac{3}{4}$ ft

$6\frac{2}{3}$ ft

42 tiles

3. Kima runs 5 yards every time Randy runs 4 yards. If Randy runs 24 yards, how far does Kima run?

30 yards

4. Each bead on an add-a-bead necklace costs $2. How much do 6 beads cost?

$2 $2 $2 $2
$2 $2

$12

5. In how many ways can you make two right triangles from an equilateral triangle with a single straight cut?

3 ways

6. Every time Jennifer earns a dollar she saves $0.35. If she has earned $7, how much has she saved?

$1 $1 $1 $1 $1 $1 $1

savings $0.35

$2.45

7. The Cameron family is seated at a circular table for a holiday dinner. If the third person is directly across from the ninth person, and each person is equidistant from the adjacent persons, how many people are seated at the table?

12 people

8. Mr. Gardner is building a 100-foot fence across the back of his property. If he places the fence posts 10 feet apart, how many posts will he need?

× × × × × × × × × × ×
10 ft

11 posts

Glencoe Division, Macmillan/McGraw-Hill

49

Name _____ **Date** _____

PRACTICE WORKSHEET 5-1

Estimating Products and Quotients

Estimate. **Answers may vary. Typical answers are given.**

1. $4\frac{1}{3} \times 3$ **12**
2. $2\frac{1}{3} \times 1\frac{7}{8}$ **4**
3. $5\frac{7}{8} \times 3\frac{8}{9}$ **24**
4. $2\frac{1}{7} \times 3\frac{1}{6}$ **6**

5. $7\frac{7}{8} \div 1\frac{1}{3}$ **7**
6. $4\frac{8}{9} + 1\frac{1}{8}$ **5**
7. $14\frac{5}{6} \div 3\frac{1}{3}$ **5**
8. $5\frac{1}{3} + 2\frac{6}{7}$ **2**

9. $4\frac{2}{5} \times 3\frac{1}{7}$ **12**
10. $3\frac{8}{9} \times 1\frac{2}{7}$ **4**
11. $2\frac{2}{9} + 1\frac{4}{5}$ **1**
12. $27\frac{1}{3} \div 9\frac{1}{3}$ **3**

13. $6\frac{7}{8} \times \frac{7}{8}$ **7**
14. $14\frac{1}{6} \div 2\frac{3}{4}$ **5**
15. $1\frac{7}{8} + 1\frac{1}{8}$ **1**
16. $8 \times 5\frac{8}{9}$ **48**

17. $23\frac{1}{7} \div 3\frac{8}{9}$ **6**
18. $6\frac{3}{10} \times 2\frac{5}{8}$ **18**
19. $2\frac{1}{4} \times 5\frac{3}{8}$ **10**
20. $33\frac{1}{3} \div 4\frac{2}{9}$ **8**

21. $16\frac{5}{6} \div 3\frac{9}{10}$ **4**
22. $2\frac{7}{12} \times 1\frac{5}{6}$ **3**
23. $9\frac{7}{8} \times 1\frac{9}{16}$ **20**
24. $28\frac{2}{7} \div 9\frac{1}{4}$ **3**

25. Is $\frac{5}{6}$ of 3 <u>less than</u> or greater than 3?

26. Is $\frac{1}{3}$ of $2\frac{1}{2}$ <u>less than</u>, greater than, or equal to $2\frac{1}{2}$?

27. Is $\frac{3}{8}$ of $\frac{1}{2}$ <u>less than</u> or greater than 0?

28. Is $\frac{4}{5}$ of $1\frac{3}{4}$ <u>less than</u> or greater than $1\frac{3}{4}$?

29. Is $2\frac{1}{2} \div 4$ <u>less than</u> or greater than $2\frac{1}{2}$?

30. Is $3\frac{5}{8} \div \frac{2}{3}$ less than or <u>greater than</u> $3\frac{5}{8}$?

31. Is $4\frac{1}{8} \div 3\frac{1}{3}$ <u>less than</u> or greater than $4\frac{1}{8}$?

32. Is $8 \div 4\frac{2}{3}$ <u>less than</u> or greater than 8?

Glencoe Division, Macmillan/McGraw-Hill

50

Name _____ **Date** _____

PRACTICE WORKSHEET 5-2

Multiplying Fractions

Multiply.

1. $\frac{1}{2} \times \frac{1}{6}$ $\frac{1}{12}$
2. $\frac{1}{3} \times \frac{1}{2}$ $\frac{1}{6}$
3. $\frac{1}{3} \times \frac{4}{9}$ $\frac{4}{27}$

4. $\frac{3}{4} \times \frac{5}{7}$ $\frac{15}{28}$
5. $\frac{2}{3} \times \frac{7}{9}$ $\frac{14}{27}$
6. $\frac{3}{5} \times \frac{4}{7}$ $\frac{12}{35}$

7. $\frac{1}{3} \times 5$ $1\frac{2}{3}$
8. $6 \times \frac{1}{2}$ 3
9. $\frac{2}{3} \times 9$ 6

10. $\frac{7}{8} \times \frac{2}{5}$ $\frac{7}{20}$
11. $\frac{2}{3} \times \frac{3}{4}$ $\frac{1}{2}$
12. $\frac{5}{8} \times \frac{2}{5}$ $\frac{1}{4}$

13. $\frac{3}{8} \times \frac{5}{6}$ $\frac{5}{16}$
14. $\frac{3}{8} \times \frac{4}{9}$ $\frac{1}{6}$
15. $\frac{8}{9} \times \frac{3}{16}$ $\frac{1}{6}$

16. $\frac{5}{9} \times \frac{3}{5}$ $\frac{1}{3}$
17. $\frac{7}{8} \times \frac{4}{7}$ $\frac{1}{2}$
18. $\frac{15}{16} \times \frac{4}{5}$ $\frac{3}{4}$

19. $\frac{5}{6} \times \frac{3}{4}$ $\frac{5}{8}$
20. $\frac{2}{3} \times \frac{9}{10}$ $\frac{3}{5}$
21. $\frac{7}{10} \times \frac{5}{6}$ $\frac{7}{12}$

22. $\frac{4}{5} \times \frac{5}{16}$ $\frac{1}{4}$
23. $\frac{3}{10} \times \frac{6}{7}$ $\frac{9}{35}$
24. $\frac{7}{12} \times \frac{3}{14}$ $\frac{1}{8}$

25. $\frac{5}{8} \times \frac{9}{10}$ $\frac{9}{16}$
26. $\frac{7}{8} \times \frac{4}{9}$ $\frac{7}{18}$
27. $\frac{7}{10} \times \frac{15}{16}$ $\frac{21}{32}$

28. $\frac{1}{2} \times \frac{2}{3} \times \frac{3}{4}$ $\frac{1}{4}$
29. $\frac{1}{2} \times \frac{1}{3} \times \frac{4}{7}$ $\frac{2}{21}$
30. $\frac{5}{16} \times \frac{3}{5} \times \frac{6}{6}$ $\frac{5}{16}$

31. $\frac{5}{12} \times \frac{4}{5} \times \frac{3}{4}$ $\frac{1}{4}$
32. $\frac{7}{8} \times \frac{3}{14} \times \frac{7}{9}$ $\frac{7}{48}$
33. $\frac{13}{16} \times \frac{8}{9} \times \frac{2}{3}$ $\frac{13}{27}$

Solve.

34. What is $\frac{1}{2}$ of $\frac{2}{3}$ cup of sugar? $\frac{1}{3}$ **cup**

35. What is $\frac{3}{4}$ of a 3-pound box of raisins? $2\frac{1}{4}$ **pounds**

Glencoe Division, Macmillan/McGraw-Hill

51

Name _____ **Date** _____

PRACTICE WORKSHEET 5-3

Multiplying Mixed Numbers

Multiply.

1. $2\frac{1}{8} \times 4\frac{4}{5}$ $10\frac{1}{5}$
2. $2\frac{3}{4} \times 1\frac{2}{3}$ $4\frac{7}{12}$
3. $1\frac{5}{8} \times 1\frac{1}{2}$ $2\frac{7}{16}$

4. $6\frac{3}{10} \times 3\frac{1}{3}$ 21
5. $3\frac{4}{5} \times 2\frac{2}{3}$ $10\frac{2}{15}$
6. $2\frac{1}{10} \times 2\frac{1}{7}$ $4\frac{1}{2}$

7. $1\frac{1}{5} \times 3\frac{1}{8}$ $3\frac{3}{4}$
8. $5\frac{1}{2} \times 2\frac{2}{3}$ $14\frac{2}{3}$
9. $6\frac{2}{3} \times 2\frac{1}{10}$ 14

10. $2\frac{2}{7} \times 4\frac{3}{8}$ 10
11. $2\frac{1}{2} \times 1\frac{3}{5}$ 4
12. $3\frac{1}{2} \times 1\frac{3}{5}$ $5\frac{3}{5}$

13. $4\frac{2}{3} \times 1\frac{7}{8}$ $8\frac{3}{4}$
14. $3\frac{3}{4} \times 2\frac{4}{5}$ $10\frac{1}{2}$
15. $7\frac{1}{3} \times 2\frac{5}{11}$ 18

16. $3\frac{1}{2} \times 3\frac{1}{2}$ $12\frac{1}{4}$
17. $1\frac{1}{5} \times 2\frac{3}{4}$ $3\frac{3}{10}$
18. $1\frac{5}{8} \times 3\frac{5}{6}$ $6\frac{2}{15}$

19. $3\frac{6}{10} \times 8\frac{1}{12}$ $29\frac{1}{10}$
20. $4\frac{3}{7} \times 1\frac{4}{5}$ $7\frac{34}{35}$
21. $3\frac{2}{3} \times 5\frac{1}{4}$ $19\frac{1}{4}$

22. $6\frac{3}{7} \times 2\frac{5}{8}$ $16\frac{7}{8}$
23. $3\frac{1}{5} \times 2\frac{5}{16}$ $7\frac{2}{5}$
24. $4\frac{3}{5} \times 3\frac{1}{3}$ $15\frac{1}{3}$

25. $2\frac{3}{4} \times \frac{2}{5} \times 8$ $8\frac{4}{5}$
26. $3\frac{1}{3} \times \frac{3}{8} \times 2\frac{1}{6}$ $2\frac{17}{24}$
27. $4\frac{1}{2} \times 2\frac{1}{4} \times 2\frac{2}{3}$ 27

Solve.

28. A hose fills $\frac{5}{16}$ of a bucket in one minute. How much of a bucket will it fill in 3 minutes?

$\frac{15}{16}$ **bucket**

29. Gae proofread $5\frac{2}{3}$ pages in one hour. How many pages can she proofread in $7\frac{1}{2}$ hours?

$42\frac{1}{2}$

Glencoe Division, Macmillan/McGraw-Hill

52

159

Glencoe Division, Macmillan/McGraw-Hill

ANSWER KEY

Name _____ Date _____

PRACTICE WORKSHEET 5-4

Applications: Energy and Coal

The chart gives the energy equivalents for one year of appliance operation.

Use the chart to find the energy equivalent in tons of coal for using each appliance.

Appliance	Energy Equivalent in Tons of Coal
Range	$\frac{1}{2}$
Microwave oven	$\frac{1}{10}$
Water heater	2
Lighting a 6-room house	$\frac{1}{3}$
Refrigerator	1
Radio	$\frac{1}{20}$
Dishwasher	$\frac{1}{5}$
Color TV	$\frac{1}{4}$

1. lighting a 6-room house for 3 years
   1 ton

2. a range for $\frac{1}{2}$ year
   $\frac{1}{4}$ **ton**

3. a color TV for 3 years
   $\frac{3}{4}$ **ton**

4. a water heater for $\frac{1}{4}$ year
   $\frac{1}{2}$ **ton**

5. a microwave oven for $\frac{3}{4}$ year
   $\frac{3}{40}$ **ton**

6. a radio for 4 years
   $\frac{1}{5}$ **ton**

7. a range for 1 month
   $\frac{1}{24}$ **ton**

8. lighting a 6-room house for 7 months
   $\frac{7}{36}$ **ton**

9. a microwave oven and a dishwasher for 1 year
   $\frac{3}{10}$ **ton**

10. a water heater and a range for 2 years
    5 tons

11. a radio and a color TV for $\frac{1}{2}$ year
    $\frac{3}{20}$ **ton**

Glencoe Division, Macmillan/McGraw-Hill

53

Name _____ Date _____

PRACTICE WORKSHEET 5-5

Problem-Solving Strategy: Simplifying the Problem

Solve.

On Monday, or day number 1, Sarah, Rich, and Claire heard a funny joke on the radio. These people each told the joke to 3 more people on day number 2, who each told the joke to 3 more people on day number 3. The pattern continued.

1. How many days passed before 100 people heard the joke?
   4 days

2. How many people heard the joke on day 6? By the end of day 6, how many people altogether had heard the joke?
   729 people; 1,092 people

3. The summer camp has 7 buildings arranged in a circle. Paths must be constructed joining every building to every other building. How many paths are needed?
   21 paths

4. In a basketball tournament, each team plays until it loses a game, then it is out of the tournament. If 64 teams are in the tournament at the start, how many games must be played to determine the tournament winner?
   63 games

5. Four people can unpack 24 crates in 2 hours. How many crates can 5 people unpack in 3 hours?
   45 crates

6. A loaf of raisin bread needs to be cut into 20 slices. How many cuts are necessary?
   19 cuts

Glencoe Division, Macmillan/McGraw-Hill

54

Name _____ Date _____

PRACTICE WORKSHEET 5-6

Dividing Fractions

Divide.

1. $4 \div \frac{1}{2}$ 8

2. $\frac{4}{9} \div \frac{2}{3}$ $\frac{2}{3}$

3. $\frac{5}{6} \div 5$ $\frac{1}{6}$

4. $\frac{9}{10} \div \frac{3}{5}$ $1\frac{1}{2}$

5. $\frac{8}{13} \div \frac{4}{7}$ $1\frac{1}{13}$

6. $\frac{5}{12} \div \frac{10}{11}$ $\frac{11}{24}$

7. $\frac{6}{7} \div 2$ $\frac{3}{7}$

8. $\frac{2}{15} \div \frac{2}{5}$ $\frac{1}{3}$

9. $\frac{4}{7} \div \frac{8}{11}$ $\frac{11}{14}$

10. $8 \div \frac{2}{3}$ 12

11. $\frac{3}{5} \div \frac{6}{7}$ $\frac{7}{10}$

12. $\frac{1}{9} \div \frac{5}{6}$ $\frac{2}{15}$

13. $20 \div \frac{4}{5}$ 25

14. $\frac{2}{9} \div \frac{7}{18}$ $\frac{4}{7}$

15. $\frac{7}{11} \div \frac{21}{22}$ $\frac{2}{3}$

16. $\frac{8}{15} \div \frac{12}{25}$ $1\frac{1}{9}$

17. $\frac{16}{19} \div \frac{4}{5}$ $1\frac{1}{19}$

18. $\frac{5}{12} \div \frac{5}{8}$ $\frac{2}{3}$

19. $\frac{14}{17} \div \frac{21}{23}$ $\frac{46}{51}$

20. $\frac{9}{11} \div \frac{3}{4}$ $1\frac{1}{11}$

21. $18 \div \frac{21}{25}$ $21\frac{3}{7}$

22. $\frac{6}{13} \div 2$ $\frac{3}{13}$

23. $\frac{13}{16} \div \frac{5}{32}$ $5\frac{1}{5}$

24. $\frac{11}{12} \div \frac{7}{24}$ $3\frac{1}{7}$

Solve.

25. Rosa's birthday cake was cut into pieces such that each piece was $\frac{1}{32}$ of the entire cake. If $\frac{3}{4}$ of the cake was eaten, how many pieces were eaten?
    24 pieces

Glencoe Division, Macmillan/McGraw-Hill

55

Name _____ Date _____

PRACTICE WORKSHEET 5-7

Dividing Mixed Numbers

Divide.

1. $3 \div 1\frac{1}{3}$ $2\frac{1}{4}$

2. $14 \div 1\frac{3}{4}$ 8

3. $\frac{5}{7} \div 2\frac{1}{7}$ $\frac{1}{3}$

4. $1\frac{4}{5} \div \frac{3}{5}$ 3

5. $4\frac{5}{6} \div 3\frac{5}{9}$ $1\frac{17}{70}$

6. $2\frac{1}{4} \div 6$ $\frac{3}{8}$

7. $2\frac{4}{7} \div 1\frac{1}{4}$ $2\frac{2}{35}$

8. $3\frac{1}{8} \div 4\frac{7}{8}$ $\frac{25}{39}$

9. $10\frac{2}{7} \div 6\frac{1}{7}$ $1\frac{29}{43}$

10. $3\frac{5}{7} \div \frac{6}{22}$ $13\frac{13}{21}$

11. $\frac{7}{15} \div 1\frac{5}{15}$ $\frac{7}{17}$

12. $3\frac{8}{9} \div 1\frac{13}{15}$ $2\frac{1}{12}$

13. $12 \div 3\frac{3}{7}$ $3\frac{1}{2}$

14. $2\frac{8}{9} \div \frac{3}{9}$ $8\frac{2}{3}$

15. $\frac{4}{5} \div 1\frac{7}{10}$ $\frac{8}{17}$

16. $\frac{4}{5} \div 3\frac{1}{2}$ $\frac{8}{35}$

17. $2\frac{1}{3} \div 8$ $\frac{7}{24}$

18. $1\frac{1}{5} \div 2\frac{5}{8}$ $\frac{16}{35}$

19. $3\frac{3}{4} \div \frac{7}{12}$ $6\frac{3}{7}$

20. $5\frac{1}{8} \div \frac{1}{6}$ $30\frac{3}{4}$

21. $7\frac{2}{3} \div 6\frac{1}{4}$ $1\frac{7}{39}$

22. $3\frac{1}{9} \div 6\frac{1}{9}$ $\frac{28}{55}$

23. $2\frac{8}{9} \div 6\frac{2}{5}$ $\frac{25}{56}$

24. $4\frac{1}{6} \div 2\frac{1}{2}$ $1\frac{2}{3}$

25. $4\frac{1}{5} \div 4\frac{8}{9}$ $\frac{54}{55}$

26. $11\frac{1}{5} \div 3\frac{3}{5}$ $3\frac{1}{9}$

27. $3\frac{3}{5} \div 9$ $\frac{2}{5}$

28. $4\frac{9}{10} \div 1\frac{1}{20}$ $4\frac{2}{3}$

29. $1\frac{7}{20} \div 4\frac{3}{5}$ $\frac{27}{92}$

30. $7\frac{1}{2} \div 1\frac{6}{19}$ $5\frac{15}{16}$

Solve.

31. Strips $\frac{2}{9}$ of a yard wide must be cut from $4\frac{4}{9}$ yards of fabric. How many strips can be cut?
    20 strips

32. In 7 ounces of fertilizer, there are $1\frac{3}{5}$ ounces phosphorus. What part of the fertilizer is phosphorus?
    $\frac{8}{35}$

Glencoe Division, Macmillan/McGraw-Hill

56

ANSWER KEY

Name _____ Date _____

PRACTICE WORKSHEET 5-8

Changing Fractions to Decimals

Change each fraction to a decimal. Use bar notation to show a repeating decimal.

1. $\frac{3}{4}$ 0.75
2. $\frac{2}{5}$ 0.4
3. $\frac{7}{8}$ 0.875
4. $\frac{1}{3}$ $0.\overline{3}$
5. $\frac{4}{9}$ $0.\overline{4}$
6. $\frac{3}{11}$ $0.\overline{27}$
7. $\frac{17}{20}$ 0.85
8. $\frac{5}{6}$ $0.8\overline{3}$
9. $\frac{3}{16}$ 0.1875
10. $\frac{8}{33}$ $0.\overline{24}$
11. $\frac{7}{12}$ $0.58\overline{3}$
12. $\frac{14}{25}$ 0.56
13. $\frac{7}{10}$ 0.7
14. $\frac{5}{8}$ 0.625
15. $\frac{11}{15}$ $0.7\overline{3}$
16. $\frac{8}{9}$ $0.\overline{8}$
17. $\frac{15}{16}$ 0.9375
18. $\frac{1}{12}$ $0.08\overline{3}$
19. $\frac{7}{20}$ 0.35
20. $\frac{5}{18}$ $0.2\overline{7}$
21. $\frac{3}{10}$ 0.3
22. $\frac{2}{15}$ $0.1\overline{3}$
23. $\frac{23}{50}$ 0.46
24. $\frac{21}{25}$ 0.84

Change each fraction to a mixed decimal.

25. $\frac{2}{3}$ $0.66\frac{2}{3}$
26. $\frac{5}{7}$ $0.71\frac{3}{7}$
27. $\frac{4}{11}$ $0.36\frac{4}{11}$
28. $\frac{7}{9}$ $0.77\frac{7}{9}$
29. $\frac{1}{6}$ $0.16\frac{2}{3}$
30. $\frac{5}{12}$ $0.41\frac{2}{3}$
31. $\frac{11}{30}$ $0.36\frac{2}{3}$
32. $\frac{2}{9}$ $0.22\frac{2}{9}$
33. $\frac{4}{15}$ $0.26\frac{2}{3}$

Glencoe Division, Macmillan/McGraw-Hill   57

Name _____ Date _____

PRACTICE WORKSHEET 5-9

Changing Decimals to Fractions

Change each decimal to a fraction.

1. 0.54 $\frac{27}{50}$
2. 0.06 $\frac{3}{50}$
3. 0.75 $\frac{3}{4}$
4. 0.48 $\frac{12}{25}$
5. 0.9 $\frac{9}{10}$
6. 0.005 $\frac{1}{200}$
7. 0.25 $\frac{1}{4}$
8. 0.625 $\frac{5}{8}$
9. 0.375 $\frac{3}{8}$
10. 0.4 $\frac{2}{5}$
11. 0.45 $\frac{9}{20}$
12. 0.62 $\frac{31}{50}$
13. 0.096 $\frac{12}{125}$
14. 0.357 $\frac{357}{1,000}$
15. 0.225 $\frac{9}{40}$
16. 0.79 $\frac{79}{100}$
17. 0.256 $\frac{32}{125}$
18. 0.08 $\frac{2}{25}$
19. 0.006 $\frac{3}{500}$
20. 0.126 $\frac{63}{500}$
21. 0.875 $\frac{7}{8}$

Change each mixed decimal to a fraction.

22. $0.55\frac{5}{9}$ $\frac{5}{9}$
23. $0.66\frac{2}{3}$ $\frac{2}{3}$
24. $0.27\frac{3}{11}$ $\frac{3}{11}$
25. $0.16\frac{2}{3}$ $\frac{1}{6}$
26. $0.57\frac{1}{7}$ $\frac{4}{7}$
27. $0.41\frac{2}{3}$ $\frac{5}{12}$

Write <, >, or = in each ○ to make a true sentence.

28. $0.\overline{7}$ ⊙ $\frac{7}{10}$
29. $\frac{3}{7}$ ⊙ 0.428
30. $0.\overline{6}$ ⊙ $\frac{2}{3}$
31. 0.2 ⊙ $\frac{2}{9}$
32. 0.8 ⊙ $\frac{4}{5}$
33. 0.83 ⊙ $\frac{5}{6}$

Glencoe Division, Macmillan/McGraw-Hill   58

Name _____ Date _____

PRACTICE WORKSHEET 5-10

Problem Solving: Using Fractions

Solve. Write each fraction in simplest form.

1. XYZ stock increased $\frac{2}{5}$ one week, $\frac{3}{4}$ the second week, and $\frac{1}{3}$ the third week. What was the stock's average weekly price increase?

    $\frac{1}{2}$

2. The regular price of a tennis racket is $24. What is the sale price during the "$\frac{1}{3}$-off" sale?

    $16

3. A machine is switched off and repaired because $\frac{7}{8}$ of the bolts it produced were defective. Out of 64 bolts, how many were defective?

    56 bolts

4. There are only $2\frac{1}{4}$ yards of ribbon left on a roll. Sheila needs $\frac{1}{3}$ yard for a bow for each of 7 dolls she is making. Is there enough ribbon? If not, how much more is needed?

    no; $\frac{1}{12}$ yard

5. Tim has four $8\frac{1}{2}$-foot boards that he could use for shelves. He decided to make just 3 shelves from each board so that none would be wasted. How long will each shelf be?

    $2\frac{5}{6}$ feet

6. Four $12\frac{7}{8}$-inch pieces of molding are needed to frame a picture. Since the color may differ a little in different molding strips, Jane wants to cut the 4 pieces from the same strip. How long must the strip be?

    $51\frac{1}{2}$ inches

7. Adult shoe sizes start at size 1, which has an inside length of $8\frac{7}{12}$ inches. There is a $\frac{1}{3}$-inch difference in full sizes. How long is an adult size 5 shoe?

    $9\frac{11}{12}$ inches

8. A recipe for 12 dozen muffins calls for $4\frac{1}{2}$ cups of oatmeal. Steve wants to make only six dozen muffins. How much oatmeal should he use?

    $2\frac{1}{4}$ cups

Glencoe Division, Macmillan/McGraw-Hill   59

Name _____ Date _____

PRACTICE WORKSHEET 6-1

The Metric System

Name the place value related to each prefix.

1. kilo thousands
2. deci tenths
3. centi hundredths
4. milli thousandths
5. hecto hundreds
6. deka tens

Complete. Use the place-value chart.

7. 1 kilometer = __1,000__ meter(s)
8. 1 centimeter = __0.01__ meter(s)
9. 1 millimeter = __0.001__ meter(s)
10. 1 dekagram = __10__ gram(s)
11. 1 decigram = __0.1__ gram(s)
12. 1 hectoliter = __100__ liters(s)

Name the metric unit for each measurement.

13. 0.001 liter milliliter
14. 1,000 grams kilogram
15. 0.01 gram centigram
16. 100 meters hectometer
17. 10 meters dekameter
18. 0.1 meter decimeter

Underline the larger unit.

19. 1 deciliter or centiliter
20. 1 centigram or 1 kilogram
21. 1 hectometer or 1 millimeter
22. 1 dekaliter or 1 deciliter

Glencoe Division, Macmillan/McGraw-Hill   60

161

Glencoe Division, Macmillan/McGraw-Hill

ANSWER KEY

Name _____ Date _____

PRACTICE WORKSHEET 6-2

Measuring Length

Choose the most reasonable measurement.

1. thickness of a nickel   1.5 cm   1.5 km   <u>1.5 mm</u>

2. width of an auditorium   33 mm   <u>33 m</u>   33 km

3. length of an earthworm   <u>100 mm</u>   100 cm   100 m

Use a metric ruler to measure each item. Give the measurement to the nearest centimeter and in millimeters.

4.
6 cm, 58 mm

5.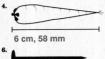
5 cm, 53 mm

6.
5 cm, 50 mm

7.
4 cm, 39 mm

8.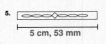
I ♥ dogs
3 cm, 32 mm

9.
1 cm, 14 mm

10.
3 cm, 26 mm

11.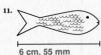
6 cm, 55 mm

Name _____ Date _____

PRACTICE WORKSHEET 6-3

Changing Metric Units

Complete.

1. 3 km = <u>3,000</u> m
2. 4 m = <u>4,000</u> mm
3. 5 mm = <u>0.5</u> cm
4. 20 km = <u>2,000,000</u> cm
5. 30 cm = <u>0.3</u> m
6. 820 mm = <u>0.82</u> m
7. 9 cm = <u>90</u> mm
8. 50 m = <u>5,000</u> cm
9. 99 m = <u>0.099</u> km
10. 5 m = <u>5,000</u> mm
11. 12 mm = <u>1.2</u> cm
12. 0.2 km = <u>20,000</u> cm
13. 39 cm = <u>0.39</u> m
14. 82 mm = <u>0.082</u> m
15. 92 cm = <u>920</u> mm
16. 1.3 m = <u>130</u> cm
17. 905 m = <u>0.905</u> km
18. 3.1 km = <u>3,100</u> m
19. 3.7 m = <u>3,700</u> mm
20. 50 mm = <u>5</u> cm
21. 0.9 km = <u>90,000</u> cm
22. 39.5 cm = <u>0.395</u> m
23. 132 cm = <u>1.32</u> m
24. 21 cm = <u>210</u> mm
25. 0.34 m = <u>34</u> cm
26. 57 m = <u>0.057</u> km

Solve.

27. The handlebars of Jackie's racing bike are 97 centimeters above the ground. How many millimeters is this?

970 mm

28. The distance from Oak Street to Main Street is 0.75 kilometers. How many meters is this?

750 m

Name _____ Date _____

PRACTICE WORKSHEET 6-4

Measuring Mass

Complete.

1. 54 g = <u>54,000</u> mg
2. 7 kg = <u>7,000</u> g
3. 8.5 kg = <u>8,500</u> g
4. 2.7 g = <u>2,700</u> mg
5. 458 g = <u>0.458</u> kg
6. 3 mg = <u>0.003</u> g
7. 78 kg = <u>78,000</u> g
8. 3,952 g = <u>3.952</u> kg
9. 16 g = <u>0.016</u> kg
10. 41.7 g = <u>41,700</u> mg
11. 4,351 mg = <u>4.351</u> g
12. 2 g = <u>0.002</u> kg
13. 906 g = <u>0.906</u> kg
14. 38 mg = <u>0.038</u> g
15. 7.5 g = <u>0.0075</u> kg
16. 6,000 g = <u>6</u> kg
17. 520 mg = <u>0.520</u> g
18. 25,480 g = <u>25.48</u> kg

Solve.

19. The King High School yearbook has a mass of 520 grams. If 430 students ordered the yearbook, what is the mass in kilograms of all these yearbooks combined?

223.6 kg

20. Sandy weighed the newspapers that she delivered last Sunday. They weighed 75 kilograms in all. If Sandy delivered 62 Sunday papers, about how much did one paper weigh?

1.2 kg

21. The total weight of 3 kittens is 8.7 kilograms. What is the average weight of each kitten in grams?

2,900 g

22. One egg weighs about 35 grams. About how much do a dozen eggs weigh in kilograms?

about 0.42 kg

Name _____ Date _____

PRACTICE WORKSHEET 6-5

Measuring Capacity

Complete.

1. 2 kL = <u>2,000</u> L
2. 5 L = <u>5,000</u> mL
3. 125 mL = <u>0.125</u> L
4. 0.52 kL = <u>520</u> L
5. 12.4 kL = <u>12,400</u> L
6. 15 L = <u>0.015</u> kL
7. 75 mL = <u>0.075</u> L
8. 309 mL = <u>0.309</u> L
9. 900 L = <u>0.9</u> kL
10. 0.06 L = <u>60</u> mL
11. 85 kL = <u>85,000</u> L
12. 3,500 L = <u>3.5</u> kL
13. 425 L = <u>0.425</u> kL
14. 29.3 L = <u>29,300</u> mL
15. 0.25 L = <u>250</u> mL
16. 0.4 kL = <u>400</u> L
17. 32 L = <u>32,000</u> mL
18. 51.3 L = <u>0.0513</u> kL

Solve.

19. The social committee figures it needs one 180-milliliter serving of punch for each of the 140 guests at the reception. How many liters of punch do they need in all?

25.2 L

20. The Adams family car has a gas tank with a capacity of 50 liters. After a trip they filled the tank with 42 liters of gas. How much gas was in the tank before they filled it?

8 L

21. Seventeen people attended the Forbes family picnic. They had 10 liters of lemonade at the start, and it was all gone at the end of the day. If each person had an equal amount of lemonade, about how many milliliters did each drink?   About 588 mL

22. The daily dosage of medicine for Joe's allergy is 2 milliliters. The bottle contained 0.24 liter when it was full. How many days will this medicine last?

120 days

ANSWER KEY

Name _____ Date _____

PRACTICE WORKSHEET 6-6

Problem-Solving Strategy: Acting It Out

Solve.

1. Twenty votes were cast for club president. You won by 4 votes over your opponent. How many votes did you receive?
12 votes

2. For every $3 your friend earned, you earned $5. How much did you earn if your friend earned $12?
$20

3. You have 4 different-colored bangle bracelets. How many different combinations of 2 or 3 bracelets can you wear?
10

4. Sue is shorter than Tom and taller than Bob. Tom is taller than Bob and shorter than Amy. Put the people in order from tallest to shortest.
Amy, Tom, Sue, Bob

5. Sam has more money than Sue. Allen has less money than Sue. Does Sam have more money than Allen?
yes

6. Four people are going out to dinner. How many different ways can the people be seated at a square table if one person only sits on each side and one person never moves?
6

7. There are 5 people. How many different committees of 3 people each can be formed?
10 committees

8. Joan lives next door to Bob. Bob lives next door to Joe. Does Joan live next door to Joe?
no

65

Name _____ Date _____

PRACTICE WORKSHEET 6-7

Customary Units of Length

Complete.

1. 3 mi = **15,840** ft
2. 4 yd = **12** ft
3. 21 ft = **7** yd
4. 72 in. = **6** ft
5. 9 mi = **15,840** yd
6. 840 in. = **70** ft
7. 1 mi = **63,360** in.
8. 84 in. = **$2\frac{1}{3}$** yd
9. 90 ft = **1,080** in.
10. 2 ft = **24** in.
11. 5 yd = **180** in.
12. 12 mi = **63,360** ft
13. 13 mi = **22,880** yd
14. 39 yd = **117** ft
15. 72 in. = **2** yd
16. 96 in. = **8** ft
17. $1\frac{1}{3}$ ft = **16** in.
18. 95 mi = **167,200** yd
19. 7,040 yd = **4** mi
20. $3\frac{1}{2}$ mi = **18,480** ft
21. 54 in. = **$4\frac{1}{2}$** ft
22. $\frac{1}{2}$ mi = **2,640** ft
23. 42 ft = **14** yd
24. 132 yd = **44** ft
25. 26,436 ft = **5** mi **36** ft
or
12 yd
26. 4,368 in. = **121** yd **1** ft

Solve.

27. The track around the field is 440 yards long. How many laps must be run to cover one mile?
4 laps

28. Marco's favorite shot in basketball is 15 feet from the basket. How many inches is that?
180 in.

66

Name _____ Date _____

PRACTICE WORKSHEET 6-8

Customary Units of Weight and Capacity

Complete.

1. 2 T = **4,000** lb
2. 16,000 lb = **8** T
3. 48 oz = **3** lb
4. 1.5 lb = **24** oz
5. 6 lb = **96** oz
6. 3 T = **6,000** lb
7. 3 lb 4 oz = **52** oz
8. $2\frac{1}{2}$ T = **5,000** lb
9. $\frac{3}{4}$ lb = **12** oz
10. 8 qt = **2** gal
11. 3 pt = **6** c
12. 12 c = **6** pt
13. 5 pt = **$2\frac{1}{2}$** qt
14. 4 gal = **16** qt
15. 18 qt = **72** c
16. 64 fl oz = **2** qt
17. $2\frac{3}{4}$ gal = **22** pt
18. $\frac{1}{2}$ c = **4** fl oz

Solve.

19. Darwin is buying fruit juice for a party. A 32-fluid-ounce bottle costs $1.19. How much will it cost for 20 one-cup servings?
$5.95

20. An 8-ounce package of ground beef costs $1.12. How much will it cost for a pound and a half of ground beef?
$3.36

67

Name _____ Date _____

PRACTICE WORKSHEET 6-9

Formulas and Temperature

Choose the better temperature.

1. drinking water, **5°C** or 45°C
2. a summer day, **25°C** or 75°C
3. hot chocolate, 50°F or **105°F**
4. a fall day, –12°C or **12°C**
5. snow, –42°F or **30°F**
6. a comfortable room, **68°F** or 20°F
7. a baking oven, **205°C** or 500°C
8. a car's engine at high speed, **90°C** or 32°C

Find the equivalent temperature to the nearest degree.

9. 7°C **45°F**
10. 35°C **95°F**
11. 272°C **522°F**
12. 58°C **136°F**
13. 163°C **325°F**
14. 118°C **244°F**
15. 54°C **129°F**
16. 67°C **153°F**
17. 12°C **54°F**

Find the equivalent temperature to the nearest degree.

18. 59°F **15°C**
19. 93°F **34°C**
20. 446°F **230°C**
21. 26°F **–3°C**
22. 84°F **29°C**
23. 41°F **5°C**
24. 72°F **22°C**
25. 122°F **50°C**
26. 107°F **42°C**

Solve.

27. Would you need to wear a sweater if the room temperature was 25°C?
no

28. Would you need to turn on the heater in the car if the temperature was 5°C?
yes

29. The noon temperature was reported at 83°F. The 6:00 P.M. temperature was 57°F. What was the drop in temperature?
26°F

30. A Canadian recipe called for an oven temperature of 230°C. About what temperature would this be in degrees Fahrenheit?
about 450°F

68

ANSWER KEY

Name _____ Date _____

PRACTICE WORKSHEET 6-10

Measuring Time
Complete.

1. 45 min = __2,700__ s
2. 4 d = __5,760__ min
3. 72 h = __3__ d
4. 3 h = __180__ min
5. 8 h = __28,800__ s
6. 7 d = __10,080__ min
7. 75 min = __1__ h __15__ min
8. 8 h 20 min = __500__ min
9. 15 h = __900__ min
10. 8 d = __192__ h
11. 3,000 min = __2__ d __2__ h
12. 10,080 s = __2__ h __48__ min

Find the elapsed time.

13. from 7:15 A.M. to 10:36 A.M.
3 h 21 min
14. from 2:48 P.M. to 9:16 P.M.
6 h 28 min
15. from 3:15 P.M. to noon
20 h 45 min
16. from midnight to 5:57 A.M.
5 h 57 min
17. from 8:40 A.M. to 5:30 P.M.
8 h 50 min
18. from 9:45 P.M. to 7:50 A.M.
10 h 5 min

Solve.

19. Bill punched the time clock at the factory at 7:55 A.M. He worked for 8 hours and 25 minutes and had a 45-minute lunch break. What time did he punch out?
5:05 P.M.
20. Lorie worked six days last week. She worked 7 hours and 15 minutes each day. She gets paid overtime for time worked over 40 hours in a week. How much overtime did she work?
$3\frac{1}{2}$ h

Glencoe Division, Macmillan/McGraw-Hill

69

Name _____ Date _____

PRACTICE WORKSHEET 6-11

Applications: Time Cards
Compute the working hours for each day.

1.
IN	OUT
7:00	11:00
12:00	16:00

8 h

2.
IN	OUT
9:30	12:30
13:00	16:30

6 h 30 min

3.
IN	OUT
8:45	12:15
13:15	16:15

6 h 30 min

4.
IN	OUT
9:00	11:50
12:30	17:00

7 h 20 min

5.
IN	OUT
7:50	11:30
12:15	17:05

8 h 30 min

6.
IN	OUT
10:35	14:00
14:30	19:15

8 h 10 min

7.
IN	OUT
7:45	11:45
12:15	16:45

8 h 30 min

8.
IN	OUT
13:30	16:45
17:15	21:20

7 h 20 min

9.
IN	OUT
8:25	12:00
12:45	17:15

8 h 5 min

10.
IN	OUT
12:20	16:15
16:45	21:30

8 h 40 min

11.
IN	OUT
7:15	11:30
12:15	16:00

8 h

12.
IN	OUT
11:50	17:05
17:45	20:15

7 h 45 min

Solve.

13. Michael's time card showed IN times of 8:30 and 12:45 and OUT times of 12:05 and 16:55 for Tuesday. If Michael earns $5.25 an hour, how much did he earn on Tuesday?
$40.69
14. Stacy gets paid overtime for any hours worked over 8 hours in a day. On Friday Stacy's time card showed IN times of 7:55 and 13:05 and OUT times of 12:00 and 17:30. Did Stacy work overtime on Friday? If, so how much overtime?
yes; 30 min

Glencoe Division, Macmillan/McGraw-Hill

70

Name _____ Date _____

PRACTICE WORKSHEET 6-12

Problem Solving: Using Measurements
Solve.

1. Marshall's flight is scheduled to leave Dallas at 8:46 A.M. and arrive at Chicago at 12:30 P.M. How long is the flight?
3 h 44 min
2. Six tablecloths, each 150 centimeters long, are needed to cover a row of picnic tables that have been placed end-to-end. About how many meters long is the row of tables?
about 9 m
3. On a trip, Fred bought gasoline three times — 18 gallons, 14.5 gallons, and 16.5 gallons. What was the total cost at $1.12 per gallon?
$54.88
4. If each banana has a mass of about 225 g, how much will you have to pay for 6 bananas at 64¢ per kilogram?
$0.86
5. On the first four days of her vacation, Carrie drove 215 miles, 360 miles, 280 miles, and 155 miles. What was the average daily distance?
252.5 mi
6. The weather forecast is for a low overnight of 7°C and a high tomorrow of 16°C. How many degrees will the temperature have to rise?
9°C
7. You have a bad cough for which the doctor has given you medicine. The prescribed dosage is 5 milliliters, 4 times a day. How many milliliters must be in the bottle if there is enough for 1 week?
140 mL
8. You are driving a truck loaded with bales of straw over a country road. The bridge you have crossed has posted a limit of 5 tons. Your truck weighs about 5,000 pounds and each of the 80 bales of straw weighs about 50 pounds. Is it safe for you to cross the bridge? What is the greatest number of bales you can safely haul across the bridge?
yes; 100 bales

Glencoe Division, Macmillan/McGraw-Hill

71

Name _____ Date _____

PRACTICE WORKSHEET 7-1

Basic Terms of Geometry
Use symbols to name the line segment between each pair of cities in as many ways as possible.

1. Rochester and Tomah $\overline{RT}, \overline{TR}$
2. Chicago and Milwaukee $\overline{CM}, \overline{MC}$
3. Eau Claire and Green Bay $\overline{EG}, \overline{GE}$
4. St. Paul and Rochester $\overline{SR}, \overline{RS}$

Name two other real-life models for each figure.   Answers may vary. Sample answers are given.

5. point: pencil tip
pen point; nail point
6. ray: flashlight beam
sunbeam; radar beam
7. line segment: pencil
flag pole; crossbar on goalpost
8. part of a plane: desktop
door; sidewalk

Use symbols to name each ray and line segment in the drawing at the right. Some rays may be named in different ways.

9. 12 rays
$\overrightarrow{OA}, \overrightarrow{CA}, \overrightarrow{OB}, \overrightarrow{DB},$
$\overrightarrow{AO}, \overrightarrow{CO}, \overrightarrow{OC}, \overrightarrow{AC},$
$\overrightarrow{OD}, \overrightarrow{BD}, \overrightarrow{BO}, \overrightarrow{DO}$
10. 6 line segments
$\overline{AO}, \overline{OC}, \overline{AC},$
$\overline{BO}, \overline{OD}, \overline{BD}$

Use words and symbols to name each figure in as many ways as possible.

11.
$\overline{RS}; \overline{SR};$
line segment RS;
line segment SR
12.
$\overleftrightarrow{KJ}; \overleftrightarrow{JK};$
line KJ; line JK
13.
$\overrightarrow{PQ};$ ray PQ

Glencoe Division, Macmillan/McGraw-Hill

72

164

Glencoe Division, Macmillan/McGraw-Hill

ANSWER KEY

Name _____ Date _____

PRACTICE WORKSHEET 7-2

Measuring Angles

Measure each angle shown in the figure at the right.

1. ∠ AND   76°
2. ∠ END   23°
3. ∠ GNB   77°
4. ∠ FNE   11°
5. ∠ GNA   135°
6. ∠ HND   104°
7. ∠ FNB   78°
8. ∠ CNF   61°

Measure each angle in triangle A and triangle B.

9. 50°
10. 65°
11. 65°
12. 60°
13. 90°
14. 30°

Make a drawing of each angle.   See students' work.

15. 45°   16. 30°   17. 105°

73

Name _____ Date _____

PRACTICE WORKSHEET 7-3

Classifying Angles

Classify each angle as right, acute, or obtuse.

1. obtuse   2. obtuse   3. right   4. acute

5. acute   6. acute   7. obtuse   8. obtuse

Use the figure at the right to classify each angle as right, acute, or obtuse.

9. ∠AND   acute
10. ∠BNF   obtuse
11. ∠GND   right
12. ∠ANF   obtuse
13. ∠DNH   obtuse
14. ∠ENF   acute
15. ∠CND   acute
16. ∠ENC   acute
17. ∠GNE   acute
18. ∠HNB   obtuse

Use the drawings at the right to complete the following.   See students' work.

19. Find four examples of right angles. Mark their sides on the drawings, and label these angles R.

20. Find two examples of acute angles. Mark their sides on the drawings, and label these angles A.

21. Find five examples of obtuse angles. Mark their sides on the drawings, and label these angles O.

74

Name _____ Date _____

PRACTICE WORKSHEET 7-4

Applications: Congruent Figures and Constructions

Construct a line segment congruent to each line segment. Then bisect each line segment.   See students' work.

1. A _____ B

2. C _____ D

Construct an angle congruent to each angle.   See students' work.

3.

4.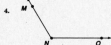

5.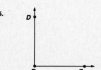

75

Name _____ Date _____

PRACTICE WORKSHEET 7-5

Parallel and Perpendicular Lines

State whether each pair of lines is parallel, perpendicular, or skew. Use symbols to name all parallel and perpendicular lines.

1. parallel; $\overleftrightarrow{ST} \parallel \overleftrightarrow{BC}$
2. skew
3. parallel; $\overleftrightarrow{TU} \parallel \overleftrightarrow{JK}$
4. perpendicular; $\overleftrightarrow{AB} \perp \overleftrightarrow{PQ}$
5. parallel; $\overleftrightarrow{MN} \parallel \overleftrightarrow{YZ}$
6. perpendicular; $\overleftrightarrow{GH} \perp \overleftrightarrow{UV}$

Use symbols to name the figures in each drawing.

7. all pairs of parallel lines
   $\overleftrightarrow{AE} \parallel \overleftrightarrow{BD}$

8. all pairs of perpendicular lines
   $\overleftrightarrow{AE} \perp \overleftrightarrow{FC}$; $\overleftrightarrow{BD} \perp \overleftrightarrow{FC}$

9. all line segments parallel to $\overline{LM}$
   $\overline{ON}, \overline{QR}, \overline{PS}$

10. all line segments perpendicular to $\overline{OP}$
    $\overline{QP}, \overline{PS}, \overline{LO}, \overline{NO}$

11. all line segments skew to $\overline{QP}$
    $\overline{LM}, \overline{NO}, \overline{MR}, \overline{NS}$

76

ANSWER KEY

Name _____ Date _____

PRACTICE WORKSHEET 7-6

Polygons

Complete the chart.

	Name	Prefix	Number of Sides	Number of Angles
1.	triangle	tri-	3	3
2.	quadrilateral	quad-	4	4
3.	pentagon	penta-	5	5
4.	hexagon	hexa-	6	6
5.	octagon	octa-	8	8
6.	decagon	deca-	10	10

Draw an example of each polygon.

7. not regular decagon
8. not regular pentagon
9. regular quadrilateral
10. regular hexagon

Name each by the number of sides. Then state whether it is regular or not regular.

11. pentagon; not regular
12. quadrilateral; regular
13. quadrilateral; not regular
14. triangle; regular
15. hexagon; regular
16. octagon; not regular

Glencoe Division, Macmillan/McGraw-Hill

77

PRACTICE WORKSHEET 7-7

Triangles

Classify each triangle by its sides and then by its angles.

1. scalene; acute
2. isosceles; right
3. equilateral; acute
4. isosceles; obtuse

Draw an example of each triangle.   See students' work.

5. equilateral triangle
6. isosceles triangle
7. scalene triangle

8. acute triangle
9. right triangle
10. obtuse triangle

11. Measure the three angles of each of the triangles you drew in Exercises 5–10. What is the sum of the measures of the angles for each triangle? What conclusion would you make?

180°; the sum of the measures of the angles of any triangle equals 180°

Glencoe Division, Macmillan/McGraw-Hill

78

PRACTICE WORKSHEET 7-8

Quadrilaterals

Classify each quadrilateral.

1. rectangle
2. square
3. trapezoid
4. rhombus
5. parallelogram

State whether each statement is true or false.

6. All trapezoids are parallelograms.
false

7. Some quadrilaterals are squares.
true

8. Some rhombuses are squares.
true

9. Some rectangles are squares.
true

10. Every parallelogram is a rectangle.
false

11. Not every quadrilateral is a parallelogram.
true

Use the quadrilaterals below to complete Exercises 12 and 13.

86° 88° 103° 83°

101° 107° 58° 94°

12. Measure and record the measure of each angle of both quadrilaterals.

13. What is the sum of the measures of the angles of each quadrilateral?
360°

Glencoe Division, Macmillan/McGraw-Hill

79

PRACTICE WORKSHEET 7-9

Three-Dimensional Figures

Name each shape.

1. cylinder
2. pentagonal pyramid
3. triangular prism
4. cone

Make a drawing of each three-dimensional figure.

5. rectangular pyramid
6. cone
7. hexagonal prism
See students' work.

Copy and complete.

	Polyhedron	Number of Faces (F)	Number of Vertices (V)	Number of Edges (E)
8.	Rectangular Prism	6	8	12
9.	Triangular Pyramid	4	4	6
10.	Hexagonal Prism	8	12	18
11.	Rectangular Pyramid	5	5	8
12.	Hexagonal Pyramid	7	7	12
13.	Triangular Prism	5	6	9
14.	Octagonal Prism	10	16	24
15.	Octagonal Pyramid	9	9	16

Glencoe Division, Macmillan/McGraw-Hill

80

ANSWER KEY

Name _____ Date _____

PRACTICE WORKSHEET 7-10

Problem – Solving Strategy: Use Logical Reasoning

Which one does not belong? Explain your answer.

1. a. b. c. d.

   b; has a curved surface

2. a. b. c. d.

   c; does not have 2 pairs of parallel sides

3. a. vertex   b. face   c. ray   d. edge

   c; not part of a three-dimensional figure

4. a. rhombus   b. rectangle   c. scalene triangle   d. obtuse triangle

   a; always has congruent sides

Choose the letter of the best answer. Explain your answer.

5. line segment is to ruler as angle is to
   a. triangle   b. compass   c. protractor   d. ray

   c; a protractor is used to measure an angle.

6. triangle is 180° as quadrilateral is to
   a. 360°   b. 90°   c. 180°   d. 400°

   a; there are 360° in the measures of the angles of a quadrilateral.

7. prism is to parallellogram as pyramid is to
   a. point   b. triangle   c. base   d. vertex

   b; the sides of a pyramid are triangles.

8. line is to ray as line segment is to
   a. line   b. ray   c. point   d. angle

   c; a point is part of a line segment.

Glencoe Division, Macmillan/McGraw-Hill

81

Name _____ Date _____

PRACTICE WORKSHEET 8-1

Circumference of Circles

Find the circumference of each circle described below. Use 3.14 for π. Round decimal answers to the nearest tenth.

1. 12 in.   37.7 in.
2. 10 mi   31.4 mi
3. 5 km   15.7 km
4. 8 m   50.24 m
5. 6 cm   37.7 cm
6. 13 ft   81.6 ft

7. $d = 4.5$ cm   14.1 cm   8. $r = 15$ yd   94.2 yd   9. $d = 9$ ft   28.3 ft
10. $r = 12$ in.   75.4 in.   11. $d = 15$ in.   47.1 in.   12. $r = 50$ km   314 km
13. $d = 33$ m   103.6 m   14. $r = 5$ mm   31.4 mm   15. $d = 20$ mi   62.8 mi

Solve.

16. The West High School band is planning a formation for their halftime performance. They want to make a large circle with a diameter of 30 yards. If the 50 band members will be equally spaced, how many feet of circumference should there be between two consecutive positions?   1.9 ft

17. The garden at Central City Park has a large circular fountain in the center. The radius of the circle is 27 feet. The tiles outlining the fountain are 9 inches long. How many tiles are needed to complete the outline of the fountain?   226 tiles

18. The diameter of the earth is about 8,000 miles. What is the circumference of the earth?   25,120 mi

19. Suppose it were possible to string a wire around the earth's equator at a constant 100 feet above the earth. How much wire would be needed?   132,634,220 ft or 25,120.1 mi

Glencoe Division, Macmillan/McGraw-Hill

82

Name _____ Date _____

PRACTICE WORKSHEET 8-2

Area of Parallelograms

Find the area of each parallelogram.

1. 12 ft, 4 ft   48 ft^2
2. 9 in., 27 in.   243 in^2
3. 0.6 m, 3 m   1.8 m^2
4. 75 m, 6 m   450 m^2
5. 63 cm, 92 cm   5,796 cm^2
6. 11 cm, 8.5 cm   93.5 cm^2

7. base, 37 km   height, 12 km   444 km^2
8. base, 5 in.   height, 3.5 in.   17.5 in^2
9. base, 9 cm   height, 3.8 cm   34.2 cm^2
10. base, 41 ft   height, 75 ft   3,075 ft^2
11. base, 1.5 ft   height, 4.5 ft   6.75 ft^2
12. base, 2 km   height 0.075 km   0.15 km^2

Solve.

13. What is the area of a parallelogram with a base of 38 in. and a height of 4 in.?   152 in^2

14. If the height of a parallelogram is 6 cm and the base is 18 cm, what is its area?   108 cm^2

15. A parallelogram with an area of 180 square feet has a height of 6 feet. How long is the base?   30 ft

16. A parallelogram with a base of 4.2 meters has an area of 31.5 square meters. What is its height?   7.5 m

Glencoe Division, Macmillan/McGraw-Hill

83

Name _____ Date _____

PRACTICE WORKSHEET 8-3

Area of Triangles

Find the area of each triangle.

1. 6 m, 52 m   156 m^2
2. 15 cm, 92 cm   690 cm^2
3. 3.8 cm, 8.5 cm   16.15 cm^2
4. 4 ft, 12 ft   24 ft^2
5. $2\frac{1}{2}$, 3 ft $3\frac{3}{4}$ ft^2
6. 2 mi, 3 mi   3 mi^2

7. base, 6 km   height, 5 km   15 km^2
8. base, 4.4 in.   height, 3.5 in.   7.7 in^2
9. base, $\frac{2}{3}$ yd   height, 1 yd $\frac{1}{3}$ yd^2
10. base, 24 mm   height, 13 mm   156 mm^2
11. base, 5 mi   height, 4 mi   10 mi^2
12. base, $3\frac{2}{3}$ yd   height, $1\frac{2}{3}$ yd $3\frac{1}{18}$ yd^2

Solve.

13. A house has a triangular-shaped section of roof that measures 21 feet at the base and has a height of 14 feet. How many square feet of roofing will be needed for this section of roof?   147 ft^2

14. Jack is making a tent from a pattern. Both ends are shaped like a triangle that has a base of 8 feet and a height of 6 feet, including excess for hems. How many square feet of material will Jack use for the ends?   48 ft^2

15. A triangular-shaped section of lawn measures 15 meters at the base and has a height of 8 meters. How many square meters of grass is this?   60 m^2

16. One section of town is bordered by three streets, forming a triangle that measures 6 kilometers at the base and has a height of 4 kilometers. How many square kilometers are contained in this section of town?   12 km^2

Glencoe Division, Macmillan/McGraw-Hill

84

ANSWER KEY

PRACTICE WORKSHEET 8-4

Area of Circles

Find the area of each circle whose radius is given. Use 3.14 for π. Round decimal answers to the nearest tenth.

1. 12 in
452.2 in²

2. 15 cm
706.5 cm²

3. 5 m
78.5 m²

4. 2.6 ft
21.2 ft²

5. 18 yd
1,017.4 yd²

6. 80 mm
20,096 mm²

Find the area of each circle whose diameter is given. Use 3.14 for π. Round decimal answers to the nearest tenth.

7. 56 m
2,461.8 m²

8. 4 in.
12.6 in²

9. 12 ft
113.0 ft²

10. 9 cm
63.6 cm²

11. 2.8 km
6.2 km²

12. 40 mi
1,256 mi²

Find the area of each circle described below. Use 3.14 for π. Round decimal answers to the nearest tenth.

13.
254.3 m²

14.
201.0 ft²

15.
153.9 mm²

16.
19.6 yd²

Solve.

17. A circular fountain in Washington Park has a radius of 6 meters. How many square meters of tile are needed for the bottom of the fountain?
113.0 m²

18. A reading room at the library is circular in shape, with a diameter of 28 feet. How many square feet of carpet are needed for this room?
615.4 ft²

19. An old mansion has a large window in the shape of a semicircle. If the bottom edge is 8 feet long, what is the area of the window?
25.12 ft²

20. A sprinkler is set up at the corner of a building and is set to spray a radius of 14 meters. How many square meters of grass will the sprinkler cover?
461.6 m²

PRACTICE WORKSHEET 8-5

Applications: Installing Carpets

Find the total cost of carpeting each of the rooms pictured below. The cost per square yard of the carpeting is given.

1.
$14.50 per square yard   **$507.50**

2.
$19.95 per square yard   **$997.50**

3.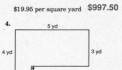
$17.00 per square yard   **$306.00**

4.
$16.99 per square yard   **$271.84**

5.
$21.50 per square yard   **$602.00**

6.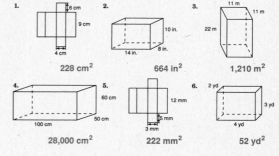
$18.00 per square yard   **$1,008.00**

PRACTICE WORKSHEET 8-6

Problem-Solving Strategy: Making a Diagram

Solve by making a diagram.

1. Darryl, Marcia, and José each work out at Sam's Gym. Darryl works out once every 2 days, Marcia every 3 days, and José every 5 days. If they are all at the gym on March 4, what is the next date they will all be at the gym?
April 3

2. It takes 5 minutes for the director to call 3 choir members and tell them the rehearsal is canceled. It takes 5 minutes for those choir members to call another 3 members each, and so on. How many choir members can be called in 20 minutes?
120 choir members

3. Of the 90 members of the freshman class, ½ participate in sports and ¾ participate in music activities. If ⅓ do not participate in sports or music, how many participate in both sports and music?
39 students

4. A gardener divides his seedlings equally among 5 gardens. In one garden he plants ¾ of the seedlings as a border and has 8 seedlings left over. How many seedlings did he start with?
160 seedlings

5. A car is available in white, black, or gray; with an automatic or manual transmission; and with 2 doors or 4 doors. In how many different combinations of color, transmission, and doors is this car available?
12 combinations

6. Hassan used part of his savings to buy a tape player for $199.95, a compact disc player for $254.99, and speakers for $175.50. He paid sales tax of $31.52 and still had ⅗ of his savings left. How much were Hassan's savings before he made these purchases?
$992.94

PRACTICE WORKSHEET 8-7

Surface Area of Rectangular Prisms

Find the surface area of each rectangular prism.

1.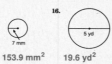
228 cm²

2.
664 in²

3.
1,210 m²

4.
28,000 cm²

5.
222 mm²

6.
52 yd²

7. length = 3 ft
width = 2 ft
height = 8 ft
92 ft²

8. length = 16 cm
width = 4 cm
height = 9 cm
488 cm²

9. length = 9 in.
width = 5 in.
height = 27 in.
846 in²

10. length = 8 m
width = 8 m
height = 6 m
320 m²

11. length = 8 yd
width = 2 yd
height = 4 yd
112 yd²

12. An artist made a large sculpture in the shape of a rectangular prism. It was 8 ft long by 3 ft wide by 5 ft high. What was its surface area?
158 ft²

13. The 8 ft by 5 ft sides of the sculpture were painted red. The 3 ft by 8 ft sides were painted blue, and the other sides were painted white. How many square feet were painted each color?
red: 80 ft²; blue: 48 ft²; white: 30 ft²

ANSWER KEY

PRACTICE WORKSHEET 8-8

Surface Area of Cylinders

Find the surface area of each cylinder. Use 3.14 for π. Round decimal answers to the nearest tenth.

1. (6 cm, 9 cm, 6 cm)
565.2 cm^2

2. (10 in., 14 in.)
1,507.2 in^2

3. (22 m, 11 m)
4,559.3 m^2

4. (60 m, 50 m)
41,448 m^2

5. (5 mm, 12 mm, 5 mm)
533.8 mm^2

6. (1 ft, 9 ft)
62.8 ft^2

7. radius = 3 ft
height = 8 ft
207.2 ft^2

8. radius = 16 cm
height = 9 cm
2,512 cm^2

9. radius = 9 in.
height = 27 in.
2,034.7 in^2

10. radius = 8 m
height = 6 m
703.4 m^2

11. radius = 8 yd
height = 4 yd
602.9 yd^2

12. radius = 4 m
height = 6.5 m
263.8 m^2

PRACTICE WORKSHEET 8-9

Volume of Rectangular Prisms

Find the volume of each rectangular prism described below.

1. (10 in., 14 in., 8 in.)
1,120 in^3

2. (11 m, 11 m, 22 m)
2,662 m^3

3. (2 yd, 4 yd, 3 yd)
24 yd^3

4. (7 cm, 7 cm, 7 cm)
343 cm^3

5. (8.5 in., 1 in., 3 in.)
25.5 in^3

6. (2.5 m, 9.2 m, 4 m)
92 m^3

7. l = 12 ft
w = 8 ft
h = 7 ft
672 ft^3

8. l = 5.2 mm
w = 12 mm
h = 4 mm
249.6 mm^3

9. l = 26 cm
w = 19 cm
h = 21 cm
10,374 cm^3

10. l = 4 in.
w = 17 in.
h = 3 in.
204 in^3

11. l = 1.3 m
w = 7 m
h = 2 m
18.2 m^3

12. l = 4 yd
w = 4 yd
h = 6 yd
96 yd^3

PRACTICE WORKSHEET 8-10

Volume of Pyramids

Find the volume of each pyramid.

1. (14 in., 8 in., 8 in.)
298.7 in^3

2. (9 m, 6 m, 4 m)
72 m^3

3. (8 cm, 12 cm, 12 cm)
384 cm^3

4. (6 ft, 7 ft, 2 ft)
28 ft^3

5. (12 mm, 3 mm, 3 mm)
36 mm^3

6. (10 in., 5.2 in., 4.6 in.)
79.7 in^3

7. l = 12 ft
w = 12 ft
h = 7 ft
336 ft^3

8. l = 5.8 m
w = 4 m
h = 9 m
69.6 m^3

9. l = 9 in.
w = 9 in.
h = 16 in.
432 in^3

10. l = 8 m
w = 3 m
h = 11 m
88 m^3

11. l = 13 cm
w = 7.5 cm
h = 10 cm
325 cm^3

12. l = 15 mm
w = 15 mm
h = 17 mm
1,275 mm^3

PRACTICE WORKSHEET 8-11

Volume of Cylinders

Find the volume of each cylinder. Use 3.14 for π. Round decimal answers to the nearest tenth.

1. (8 in., 42 in.)
8,440.3 in^3

2. (32 ft, 4 ft)
1,607.7 ft^3

3. (2 yd, 8 yd)
100.5 yd^3

4. (15 cm, 35 cm)
24,727.5 cm^3

5. (30 mm, 12 mm)
13,564.8 mm^3

6. (60 m, 75 m)
847,800 m^3

7. radius, 10 ft
height, 8 ft
2,512 ft^3

8. radius, 5 cm
height, 19 cm
1,491.5 cm^3

9. diameter, 14 m
height, 9 m
1,384.7 m^3

10. radius, 9 in.
height, 27 in.
6,867.2 in^3

11. diameter, 16 yd
height, 11 yd
2,210.6 yd^3

12. radius, 6 m
height, 57 m
6,443.3 m^3

ANSWER KEY

Name _____ Date _____

PRACTICE WORKSHEET 8-12

Volume of Cones

Find the volume of each cone described below. Round decimal answers to the nearest tenth.

1. 234.5 in^3

2. 84.8 mm^3

3. 301.4 cm^3

4. 923.2 ft^3

5. $2,967.3 \text{ mm}^3$

6. 565.2 in^3

7. radius, 12 ft
height, 8 ft
$1,205.8 \text{ ft}^3$

8. diameter, 28 m
height, 9 m
$1,846.3 \text{ m}^3$

9. radius, 10 in.
height, 25 in.
$2,616.7 \text{ in}^3$

10. diameter, 16 yd
height, 11 yd
736.9 yd^3

11. diameter, 10 cm
height, 5 cm
130.8 cm^3

12. radius, 27 cm
height, 19 cm
$14,497.4 \text{ cm}^3$

Name _____ Date _____

PRACTICE WORKSHEET 8-13

Problem Solving: Using Area and Volume

Solve. Round decimal answers to the nearest tenth.

1. Rita is planting English ivy. She needs 6 plants to cover 10 square feet of ground. How many plants does she need to cover a rectangular area 20 feet long and 15 feet wide?
180 plants

2. Twelve boxes of detergent are to be placed in a carton. Each box is 8 in. by 3 in. by 11 in. How much space must the carton contain? Give possible dimensions of the carton.
$3,168 \text{ in}^3$;
possible dimensions:
16 in. by 9 in. by 22 in.

3. A circular swimming pool is to be dug. It is to have a diameter of 20 ft and a depth of 6 ft. How much dirt must be removed?
$1,884 \text{ ft}^3$

4. The weather service issued a severe storm warning for all counties within a 50-mile radius of Plainview. What is the area covered by the warning?
$7,850 \text{ mi}^2$

5. A cord of wood is equivalent to 128 cubic feet and is usually described as 4 ft by 4 ft by 8 ft. Herman helps his dad cut wood, which they sell. They have a stack 16 ft by 16 ft by 12 ft. How may cords of wood do they have ready for sale?
24 cords

6.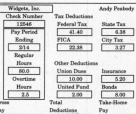

The dining, living, and hall areas are to be carpeted. How much will it cost if the carpet is priced at 412.89 per square yard?
$438.26

Name _____ Date _____

PRACTICE WORKSHEET 9-1

Ratio

Write each ratio as a fraction in simplest form.

1. 6 losses to 13 wins $\frac{6}{13}$

2. 4 inches of snow in 9 days $\frac{4}{9}$

3. 21 wins to 14 losses $\frac{3}{2}$

4. 15 children out of 60 passengers $\frac{1}{4}$

5. 12 losses in 52 games $\frac{3}{13}$

6. 24 passengers in 8 cars $\frac{3}{1}$

7. 18 tickets for $54 $\frac{1}{3}$

8. 27 wins to 18 losses $\frac{3}{2}$

9. 32 wins in a total of 80 games $\frac{2}{5}$

10. 144 bottles in 36 cartons $\frac{4}{1}$

11. 47 women out of 94 adults $\frac{1}{2}$

12. 360 miles in 6 hours $\frac{60}{1}$

Andy Peabody works for Widgets, Inc. Use his check stub to write a ratio that compares the following. (Do not write in simplest form.)

Widgets, Inc.		Andy Peabody
Check Number	Tax Deductions	
12546	Federal Tax	State Tax
Pay Period	41.40	6.38
Ending	FICA	City Tax
2/14	22.38	3.27
Regular Hours		
80.0	Other Deductions	
Overtime	Union Dues	Insurance
Hours	10.00	5.20
2.5	United Fund	Bonds
	2.00	8.00
Gross Pay	Total Deductions	Take-Home Pay
334.02	100.63	233.39

13. overtime hours to regular hours $\frac{2.5}{80}$

14. FICA tax to gross pay $\frac{22.38}{334.02}$

15. total deductions to gross pay $\frac{100.63}{334.02}$

16. United Fund to take-home pay $\frac{2.00}{233.39}$

Solve.

17. Bolton High School's basketball team has won 12 games and lost 6 games. What is their ratio of games won to games lost? $\frac{2}{1}$

18. Brandon got 12 problems correct and 3 problems wrong on today's quiz. What was his ratio of problems correct to the total number of problems? $\frac{4}{5}$

Name _____ Date _____

PRACTICE WORKSHEET 9-2

An Introduction to Probability

A date is chosen at random from the month of February. Find the probability of choosing each date.

1. The date is the fifteenth. $\frac{1}{28}$

2. The date is a Wednesday. $\frac{1}{7}$

3. It is after the twenty-fourth. $\frac{1}{7}$

4. It is before the sixth. $\frac{5}{28}$

5. It is an even-numbered date. $\frac{1}{2}$

February						
S	M	T	W	T	F	S
	1	2	3	4	5	6
7	8	9	10	11	12	13
14	15	16	17	18	19	20
21	22	23	24	25	26	27
28						

A die is rolled once. Find the probability rolling each of the following.

6. a 5 $\frac{1}{6}$

7. a 2 $\frac{1}{6}$

8. an odd number $\frac{1}{2}$

9. a 5 or a 6 $\frac{1}{3}$

10. a number less than 3 $\frac{1}{3}$

11. not a 4 $\frac{5}{6}$

12. a number less than 1 0

13. not a 3 or a 4 $\frac{2}{3}$

14. a number less than 10 1

15. a 2, a 3, or a 4 $\frac{1}{2}$

Two dice are rolled once. The possible outcomes are listed at the right. Find each probability.

6,1	6,2	6,3	6,4	6,5	6,6
5,1	5,2	5,3	5,4	5,5	5,6
4,1	4,2	4,3	4,4	4,5	4,6
3,1	3,2	3,3	3,4	3,5	3,6
2,1	2,2	2,3	2,4	2,5	2,6
1,1	1,2	1,3	1,4	1,5	1,6

16. P(5,5) $\frac{1}{36}$

17. P(2,1) $\frac{1}{36}$

18. P(an odd sum) $\frac{1}{2}$

19. P(a sum of 7) $\frac{1}{6}$

20. P(a sum of 11) $\frac{1}{18}$

21. P(neither number 4) $\frac{25}{36}$

22. P(a product less than 8) $\frac{7}{18}$

23. P(neither number 3 or 4) $\frac{4}{9}$

24. P(a sum of 4 or 10) $\frac{1}{6}$

25. P(both numbers different) $\frac{5}{6}$

Solve.

26. A dish of nuts has 12 walnuts, 8 pecans, and 4 cashews. Bhatti takes one without looking. What is the probability it is a pecan? $\frac{1}{3}$

27. There are 15 girls and 11 boys in the class. One is chosen at random to attend a play. What is the probability that a girl is chosen? $\frac{15}{26}$

ANSWER KEY

PRACTICE WORKSHEET 9-3

Proportion

Determine if each pair of ratios forms a proportion.

1. 3 to 6, 4 to 5 N	**2.** 2 to 3, 1 to 2 N	**3.** 4 to 3, 3 to 4 N
4. 5:25, 2:10 Y	**5.** 19:20, 38:40 Y	**6.** 2:5, 11:25 N
7. 4 to 5, 24 to 25 N	**8.** 28:50, 43:53 N	**9.** 8 to 13, 32 to 52 Y
10. 30 to 24, 48 to 40 N	**11.** 35:21, 5:3 Y	**12.** 6:10 , 20:12 N
13. 3 to 6, 30 to 60 Y	**14.** 5:4, 25:16 N	**15.** 36:18, 33:15 N
16. 9:2, 27:6 Y	**17.** 400 to 4, 50 to 5 N	**18.** 9:15, 36:60 Y
19. 100 to 20, 10 to 2 Y	**20.** 2 to 7, 6 to 28 N	**21.** 125:75, 30:18 Y

97

Glencoe Division, Macmillan/McGraw-Hill

PRACTICE WORKSHEET 9-4

Solving Proportions

Solve each proportion.

1. $\frac{3}{4} = \frac{t}{12}$ 9	**2.** $\frac{5}{8} = \frac{50}{80}$ 8	**3.** $\frac{b}{8} = \frac{7}{10}$ 5.6
4. $\frac{5}{9} = \frac{70}{r}$ 126	**5.** $\frac{8}{11} = \frac{c}{44}$ 32	**6.** $\frac{15}{17} = \frac{3}{h}$ 3.4
7. $\frac{6}{18} = \frac{z}{9}$ 3	**8.** $\frac{x}{35} = \frac{4}{7}$ 20	**9.** $\frac{18}{p} = \frac{5}{11}$ 39.6
10. $\frac{21}{24} = \frac{14}{e}$ 16	**11.** $\frac{16}{d} = \frac{12}{9}$ 12	**12.** $\frac{s}{14} = \frac{6}{70}$ 1.2
13. $\frac{f}{18} = \frac{24}{9}$ 48	**14.** $\frac{32}{48} = \frac{4}{z}$ 6	**15.** $\frac{2}{21} = \frac{g}{84}$ 8
16. $\frac{36}{y} = \frac{8}{12}$ 54	**17.** $\frac{t}{4} = \frac{51}{18}$ $11.\overline{3}$ or $11\frac{1}{3}$	**18.** $\frac{6}{7} = \frac{24}{c}$ 28
19. $\frac{13}{52} = \frac{k}{8}$ 2	**20.** $\frac{35}{w} = \frac{25}{5}$ 7	**21.** $\frac{m}{90} = \frac{31}{9}$ 310

98

Glencoe Division, Macmillan/McGraw-Hill

PRACTICE WORKSHEET 9-5

Scale Drawings

Find the actual distances. Use the scale drawing of the tennis court at the right.

1. What is the length of the entire court? **78 ft**

2. What is the width of the court for singles? **27 ft**

3. What is the width of the court for doubles? **36 ft**

4. What is the distance from the service line to the net? **21 ft**

5. What is the height of the net? **3 ft**

6. What is the distance from the base line to the nearest service line? **18 ft**

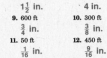

Find the distance on a scale drawing for each actual distance. The scale is 1 in.:800 ft.

7. 1,200 ft $1\frac{1}{2}$ in.	**8.** 3,200 ft 4 in.
9. 600 ft $\frac{3}{4}$ in.	**10.** 300 ft $\frac{3}{8}$ in.
11. 50 ft $\frac{1}{16}$ in.	**12.** 450 ft $\frac{9}{16}$ in.

Solve. Use the scale 1 in.:8 ft.

13. If a classroom measures 20 feet by 32 feet, what are the dimensions of the room on the scale drawing?

$2\frac{1}{2}$ in. by 4 in.

14. The cafeteria of the school is shown on the drawing as being 10 inches by $12\frac{1}{2}$ inches. What are the actual dimensions of the cafeteria?

80 ft by 100 ft

99

Glencoe Division, Macmillan/McGraw-Hill

PRACTICE WORKSHEET 9-6

Similar Figures

Find the missing length for each pair of similar figures.

1.

2.

4 m · · · · · · · · · 7.5 m

3.

4.

350 in. · · · · · · · · 1.1 cm

5.

6.

56 mm · · · · · · · · · 90 in.

7.

8.

10 ft · · · · · · · · · · 9.6 m

100

Glencoe Division, Macmillan/McGraw-Hill

171

Glencoe Division, Macmillan/McGraw-Hill

ANSWER KEY

Name _____ Date _____

PRACTICE WORKSHEET 9-7

Applications: Planning a Trip

Solve. Use the map above.

1. What is the distance from Chicago to Denver?

   985 mi

2. What is the driving time from Los Angeles to Dallas?

   30 h 30 min

3. What is the distance from New York to Chicago via Cleveland?

   817 mi

4. What is the driving time from Denver to Chicago via Memphis?

   35 h 5 min

5. It took Mr. Chou 18 hours to drive from Denver to Minneapolis. What was his average speed?

   43.5 mph

6. How long would it take to travel from New York to Memphis if you could average 50 mph?

   22.04 h or 22 h 2.4 min

7. What is the shortest route shown from Minneapolis to Dallas?

   Minneapolis to Memphis to Dallas

8. It took the Sanchez family 34 hours to drive from Minneapolis to Dallas. What route did they most likely take?

   Minneapolis to Denver to Dallas

Name _____ Date _____

PRACTICE WORKSHEET 9-8

Ratios, Percents, and Fractions
Write each fraction as a percent.

1. $\frac{31}{100}$ 2. $\frac{3}{100}$ 3. $\frac{2}{5}$ 4. $\frac{7}{4}$

   31%   **3%**   **40%**   **175%**

5. $\frac{3}{10}$ 6. $\frac{6}{25}$ 7. $\frac{7}{8}$ 8. $\frac{9}{20}$

   30%   **24%**   **$87\frac{1}{2}$%**   **45%**

9. $\frac{4}{5}$ 10. $\frac{17}{50}$ 11. $\frac{3}{4}$ 12. $\frac{19}{25}$

   80%   **34%**   **75%**   **76%**

13. $1\frac{1}{4}$ 14. $1\frac{1}{2}$ 15. $\frac{5}{6}$ 16. $\frac{9}{50}$

   125%   **150%**   **$83\frac{1}{3}$%**   **18%**

Write each percent as a fraction in simplest form.

17. 13%   18. 3%   19. 65%   20. 46%
   $\frac{13}{100}$ $\frac{3}{100}$ $\frac{13}{20}$ $\frac{23}{50}$

21. 300%   22. 55%   23. 175%   24. 96%
   3            $\frac{11}{20}$ $1\frac{3}{4}$ $\frac{24}{25}$

25. 60%   26. 37.5%   27. 250%   28. $83\frac{1}{3}$%
   $\frac{3}{5}$ $\frac{3}{8}$ $2\frac{1}{2}$ $\frac{5}{6}$

29. $33\frac{1}{3}$%   30. 100%   31. 12%   32. 0.5%
   $\frac{1}{3}$ 1 $\frac{3}{25}$ $\frac{1}{200}$

Solve.

33. If $\frac{1}{8} = 12\frac{1}{2}$%, what percent is equivalent to $\frac{5}{8}$?

   62.5%

34. On the average, 7 people out of 28 ride the bus to work. What percent do not ride the bus to work?

   75%

Name _____ Date _____

PRACTICE WORKSHEET 9-9

Percents and Decimals
Write each decimal as a percent.

1. 0.34   2. 0.715   3. 0.04   4. 1.52
   34%   **71.5%**   **4%**   **152%**

5. 3.1   6. 0.605   7. 1.2   8. 0.6
   310%   **60.5%**   **120%**   **60%**

9. 0.79   10. 0.004   11. 7.7   12. 0.09
   79%   **0.4%**   **770%**   **9%**

13. 0.349   14. 0.1   15. 0.076   16. 5.525
   34.9%   **10%**   **7.6%**   **552.5%**

Write each percent as a decimal.

17. 65%   18. 26.3%   19. 2%   20. 1.52%
   0.65   0.263   0.02   0.0152

21. $\frac{7}{10}$%   22. 450%   23. 0.9%   24. 90%
   0.007   4.5   0.009   0.9

25. 300%   26. 0.2%   27. 79%   28. $34\frac{9}{10}$%
   3   0.002   0.79   0.349

29. 7.7%   30. $7\frac{1}{2}$%   31. 175%   32. $4\frac{1}{4}$%
   0.077   0.075   1.75   0.0425

Solve.

33. In a group of 100 people, 52 have brown hair, 29 have blond hair, and 19 people have red hair. What percent of the people have either blond or red hair?

   48%

Name _____ Date _____

PRACTICE WORKSHEET 9-10

Problem-Solving Strategy: Guess and Check
Solve. Use the guess-and-check strategy.

1. Mrs. Alvirez is three times as old as her daughter. In 12 years, she will be twice as old as her daughter. What are their ages now?

   36 and 12

2. Notebook paper can be purchased in packages of 75 or 100 sheets of paper. Niki buys 6 packages and gets 475 sheets. How many packages of 100 sheets of paper does she buy?

   1 package

3. Bus fare is 75¢. Rob needed change to ride the bus home from the shopping center. He reached in his pocket and pulled out 5 coins, none larger than a quarter, that totaled 75¢. What were the coins?

   2 quarters, 2 dimes, 1 nickel

4. The Murphys spent exactly $13 on movie tickets. Adult tickets cost $3 each. Children's tickets cost $1.75 each. They bought more children's tickets. How many of each did they buy?

   2 adult and 4 children's tickets

5. The difference between two whole numbers is 10. Their product is 375. Find the two numbers.

   15 and 25

6. Brian is four times as old as his sister Jan. In six years, Brian will be twice as old as Jan. How old is Brian now?

   12

7. Jack has 6 coins in his pocket. The coins are nickels, dimes, and quarters. The total value of the coins is 60¢. How many of each coin does Jack have?

   1 quarter, 2 dimes, 3 nickels

8. The sum of four consecutive whole numbers is 54. Find the four numbers.

   12, 13, 14, 15

ANSWER KEY

Name _____ Date _____

PRACTICE WORKSHEET 10-1

Finding the Percent of a Number

Find each percentage. Use a decimal for the percent.

1. 31% of 600	186	2. 9% of 70	6.3
3. 12% of 1,875	225	4. 38% of 4,250	1,615
5. 1% of 400	4	6. 15% of 72	10.8
7. 43% of 9,200	3,956	8. 3% of 150	4.5
9. 52% of 400	208	10. 4% of 20	0.8

Find each percentage. Use a fraction for the percent.

11. 50% of 30	15	12. 40% of 65	26
13. 20% of 70	14	14. 25% of 160	40
15. $66\frac{2}{3}$% of 360	240	16. 60% of 45	27
17. 75% of 64	48	18. 10% of 210	21
19. $33\frac{1}{3}$% of 99	33	20. 80% of 20	16

The Correa family's monthly take-home pay is $2,125. This table shows their monthly budget. Find how much the Correas spend on each expense.

Expense	Percent of take-home pay
Housing	31%
Food	37%
Clothing	15%
Entertainment	6%
Transportation	9%
Savings	2%

21. housing $658.75   22. food $786.25

23. clothing $318.75   24. entertainment $127.50

25. transportation $191.25   26. savings $42.50

Name _____ Date _____

PRACTICE WORKSHEET 10-2

Finding What Percent One Number Is of Another

Find each percent. Use an equation.

1. What percent of 50 is 7?	14%	2. 16 is what percent of 30?	$53.\overline{3}$% or $53\frac{1}{3}$%
3. What percent of 80 is 120?	150%	4. What percent of 40 is 90?	225%
5. 6 is what percent of 24?	25%	6. What percent of 15 is 5?	$33.\overline{3}$% or $33\frac{1}{3}$%
7. What percent of 20 is 29?	145%	8. 15 is what percent of 60?	25%
9. 63 is what percent of 42?	150%	10. What percent of 72 is 9?	12.5% or $12\frac{1}{2}$%
11. What percent of 80 is 4?	5%	12. 6 is what percent of 1,200?	0.5% or $\frac{1}{2}$%
13. What percent of 60 is 12?	20%	14. 8 is what percent of 32?	25%
15. What percent of 20 is 25?	125%	16. 2 is what percent of 1,000?	0.2% or $\frac{1}{5}$%

Solve.

17. A model rocket usually sells for $4.00. Jamie got an $0.80 discount. What percent of the original price is the discount? **20%**

18. Dinah bought a $50 coat for $27. What percent of the original price is the sale price? **54%**

19. Josephine put $75 down on the purchase of a $300 stereo system. She will pay the rest when it is delivered. What percent of the total price is her down payment? **25%**

20. David bought a backpack for $14. The sales tax on his purchase was $0.70. What percent of the purchase price is the sales tax? **5%**

Name _____ Date _____

PRACTICE WORKSHEET 10-3

Finding a Number When a Percent of It Is Known

Find each number. Use an equation.

1. 30% of what number is 120?	400	2. 25% of what number is 60?	240
3. 8 is 5% of what number?	160	4. 100 is 100% of what number?	100
5. 80% of what number is 40?	50	6. 12% of what number is 42?	350
7. 420 is 60% of what number?	700	8. 25% of what number is 62.5?	250
9. 25 is $62\frac{1}{2}$% of what number?	40	10. 40% of what number is 80?	200
11. 50% of what number is 350?	700	12. 200% of what number is 800?	400
13. 54 is 75% of what number?	72	14. 40% of what number is 400?	1,000
15. $33\frac{1}{3}$% of what number is 80?	240	16. 18 is $37\frac{1}{2}$% of what number?	48
17. 28% of what number is 7?	25	18. 90 is 150% of what number?	60
19. $87\frac{1}{2}$% of what number is 70?	80	20. 28 is 80% of what number?	35

Solve.

21. In a school survey, 60% of the students said they own calculators. 210 sudents said they own calculators. How many students were surveyed? **350 students**

22. The Bulldogs have won 80% of their basketball games. If they lost 4 games, how many games have they played? **20 games**

Name _____ Date _____

PRACTICE WORKSHEET 10-4

Problem-Solving Strategy: Using Venn Diagrams

Solve. Use a Venn diagram.

1. How many students take a non-English language class? **87 students**

2. How many students take both Spanish and French? **8 students**

3. How many students take both Spanish and German? **3 students**

4. How many students take all three languages? **2 students**

5. Suppose the school has 300 students. How many students do not take a language other than English? **213 students**

6. Suppose the school has 300 students. What percent of students take a non-English language? **29%**

At Highwood High School, 36 freshmen are taking woodworking, 25 freshmen are taking cooking, and 9 freshmen are taking both courses. There are 100 students in the freshmen class.

Solve.

7. Draw the Venn diagram.

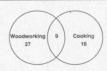

8. How many freshmen are taking only cooking? **16 freshmen**

9. How many freshmen are taking only woodworking? **27 freshmen**

10. How many freshmen are taking neither woodworking nor cooking? **48 freshmen**

Solve. Use any strategy.

11. A pizza shop offers 6 toppings on its pizzas. How many combinations of 2 toppings are possible? **15**

12. One number is $\frac{2}{3}$ of another. Their sum is 60. What are the two numbers? **24 and 36**

ANSWER KEY

Name _____ Date _____

PRACTICE WORKSHEET 10-5

Estimating the Percent of a Number

Estimate.
Answers may vary. Typical answers are given.

1. 21% of 38 — 8	**2.** 38% of 120 — 50	**3.** 27% of 82 — 20
4. 32% of 110 — 40	**5.** 146% of 52 — 75	**6.** 42% of 91 — 36
7. 79% of 203 — 160	**8.** 53% of 300 — 150	**9.** 91% of 500 — 450
10. 64% of 178 — 120	**11.** 0.5% of 600 — 3	**12.** 18% of 44 — 9
13. 41% of 60 — 25	**14.** 34% of 16 — 5	**15.** 24% of 64 — 16
16. 17% of 36 — 7	**17.** 86% of 25 — 21	**18.** 11% of 207 — 20
19. 27% of 46 — 12	**20.** 33% of 125 — 40	**21.** 48% of 76 — 40
22. 68% of 66 — 44	**23.** 39% of 52 — 20	**24.** 89% of 298 — 270
25. 63% of 40 — 24	**26.** 173% of 84 — 140	**27.** 85% of 72 — 63

Solve.

28. 24% of the cars in the parking lot were blue. If there were 87 cars in the lot, about how many of them were blue?

about 20 cars

29. Sharon got 85% of the test questions done correctly. If there were 40 test questions, how many did Sharon get right?

34 questions

Name _____ Date _____

PRACTICE WORKSHEET 10-6

Percent of Change

Find the percent of increase. Round to the nearest percent.

1. original weight, 120 lb; new weight, 125 lb — 4%	**2.** original volume, 3 L; new volume, 3.09 L — 3%
3. original price, $12; new price, $13.50 — 13%	**4.** original number, 520; new number, 640 — 23%
5. original weight, 3.2 oz; new weight, 4.2 oz — 31%	**6.** original price, $2.99; new price, $3.29 — 10%

Find the percent of decrease. Round to the nearest percent.

7. original price, $15; new price, $11 — 27%	**8.** original price, $500; new price, $450 — 10%
9. original weight, 85 lb; new weight, 78 lb — 8%	**10.** original number, 650; new number, 575 — 12%
11. original price, $9.95; new price, $6.75 — 32%	**12.** original weight, 8 kg; new weight, 7.5 kg — 6%

Solve. Round to the nearest percent.

13. A vitamin used to be packaged in bottles of 60. Now there are 75 vitamins per bottle. What is the percent of increase?

25%

14. Larry and Sue used to have 65 customers on their paper route. Now they have 59. What is the percent of decrease?

9%

15. A pair of shoes was $50 one year and $52.50 the next year. What is the percent of increase?

5%

16. Groceries cost $60 but, after redeeming coupons, the bill was $55.70. What is the percent of decrease?

7%

Name _____ Date _____

PRACTICE WORKSHEET 10-7

Discount

Find the discount and the sale price.

1. television, $500; discount rate, 15% — $75, $425	**2.** bicycle, $149.50; discount rate, 20% — $29.90, $119.60
3. typewriter, $240; discount rate, 10% — $24, $216	**4.** watch, $35.75; discount rate, 15% — $5.36, $30.39

Find the discount and the discount rate.
Round the discount rate to the nearest percent.

5. violin, $160; sale price, $140 — $20, 13%	**6.** golf clubs, $125; sale price, $99.95 — $25.05, 20%
7. fishing rod, $35; sale price, $28.50 — $6.50, 19%	**8.** computer, $795; sale price, $725 — $70, 9%
9. roller skates, $179; sale price, $150 — $29, 16%	**10.** video cassette, $20; sale price, $13.50 — $6.50, 33%
11. encyclopedia, $699; sale price, $599 — $100, 14%	**12.** cordless phone, $125; sale price, $89.99 — $35.01, 28%

Name _____ Date _____

PRACTICE WORKSHEET 10-8

Interest

Find the interest owed on each loan. Then find the total amount to be repaid.

1. principal: $300; annual rate: 12%; time: 2 years — $72; $372	**2.** principal: $750; annual rate: 8%; time: 6 months — $30; $780	**3.** principal: $4,000; annual rate: $10\frac{1}{2}$%; time: 4 years — $1,680; $5,680
4. principal: $980; annual rate: 11%; time: 24 months — $215.60; $1,195.60	**5.** principal: $30,000; annual rate: $12\frac{1}{2}$%; time: 25 years — $93,750; $123,750	**6.** principal: $1,250; rate: $1\frac{1}{2}$% per month; time: 2 months — $37.50; $1,287.50

Find the interest earned on each deposit.

7. principal: $3,340; annual rate: $5\frac{1}{2}$%; time: 8 months — $122.47	**8.** principal: $875; annual rate: 6%; time: 4 years — $210
9. principal: $1,350; annual rate: $6\frac{1}{4}$%; time: 6 months — $42.19	**10.** principal: $7,200; annual rate: $9\frac{1}{2}$%; time: $1\frac{1}{4}$ years — $855
11. principal: $5,000; annual rate: $7\frac{1}{4}$%; time: 3 years — $1,087.50	**12.** principal: $8,900; annual rate: $10\frac{1}{2}$%; time: 18 months — $1,401.75

Solve.

13. Chin borrowed $1,500 from the bank at $9\frac{1}{2}$% interest per year for 6 months. How much did he have to pay back at the end of the 6-month period?

$1,571.25

14. Sarah lent Nathan $450 at 6% annual interest to be paid back in 4 months. How much should Sarah receive when Nathan repays the loan?

$459

ANSWER KEY

Name _____ Date _____

PRACTICE WORKSHEET 10-9

Applications: Compound Interest
Find the savings total for each account.

1. principal: $400
   annual rate: 6%
   compounded quarterly
   time: 1 year
   $424.54

2. principal: $600
   annual rate: 5%
   compounded quarterly
   time: 6 months
   $615.09

3. principal: $750
   annual rate: 7%
   compounded semiannually
   time: 1 year
   $803.42

4. principal: $2,000
   annual rate: 8%
   compounded semiannually
   time: 2 years
   $2,339.72

Solve.

5. Daniel is planning to deposit $500 in one of two savings accounts. One account pays 6% simple interest. The other pays $5\frac{1}{2}$% interest compounded quarterly. In which account would he have the greater total at the end of 1 year? How much greater?
   6% simple interest; $1.92

6. Rita has $500 to deposit. The Sun Bank pays 6% interest compounded quarterly. The Star Bank pays 6% interest compounded semiannually. The Moon Bank pays 6% compounded annually. Which bank pays the most interest?
   Sun Bank

7. How much interest does each bank pay? What is the difference between the interest paid by the highest and lowest paying banks?
   Sun: $30.68; Star: $30.45; Moon: $30; $0.68

Name _____ Date _____

PRACTICE WORKSHEET 10-10

Problem Solving: Using Percent
Solve.

1. Martin saves $63 each week. If he saves 15% of his wages, how much does he earn per week?
   $420

2. Stuart wants to gain 15 pounds. This is 12% of his present weight. How much does Stuart weigh now?
   125 lb

3. During a sale, Ms. Trevino puchased a blender for 75% of the regular price. She paid $27 for the blender. What was the regular price?
   $36

4. When a truck is loaded to 45% of its capacity, there are 108 cases on the truck. How many cases will be on the truck when it is loaded to capacity?
   240 cases

5. Betty bought a camera at a 20% reduction sale. If she paid $18 for it, what was the regular price?
   $22.50

6. If 48% of the students in a school are boys, and the girls number 468, how many students are enrolled?
   900 students

7. If an ore contains 16% copper, how many tons of ore are needed to get 20 tons of copper?
   125 tons

8. Patricia Walsh receives a base salary of $125 plus a commission of 6% of sales. If her pay for one week was $441.80, what were her total sales?
   $5,280

9. Christopher Cernami answered 4 test questions incorrectly and scored 90%. How many questions did he answer correctly?
   36 questions

10. The Sluggerville baseball team won 32 games. Their percent of games lost was 20%. Find the number of games the team played.
    40 games

Name _____ Date _____

PRACTICE WORKSHEET 11-1

Median, Mode, and Range
Find the median, mode, and range for each set of data.

1. 51, 47, 48, 51, 49, 51, 52
   51, 51, 5

2. 114, 117, 114, 119, 115, 116, 112
   115, 114, 7

3. 10, 15, 10, 15, 4, 1, 4, 15, 10, 15, 11, 7
   10, 15, 14

4. 49, 52, 54, 51, 60, 57, 73, 51, 55, 57, 53, 57
   54.5, 57, 24

5. 172, 176, 172, 177, 177, 175, 175, 178, 172, 174, 177
   175, 172 and 177, 6

6. 9.2, 8.6, 9.3, 9.7, 7.2, 9.6, 9.9, 9.5, 9.4
   9.4, no mode, 2.7

7. 0.64, 1.62, 1.66, 0.62, 1.66, 0.64, 0.62, 1.62
   1.13, no mode, 1.04

8. 160, 156, 160, 315, 159, 160, 153, 251, 158, 150
   159, 160, 165

Solve.

9. Allan scored 87, 92, 85, 88, and 84 on math tests this semester. What is the median of these scores? The range?
   87; 8

10. On his next test, Allan scored 98. How does this affect the median? How does it affect the range?
    increased to 87.5; increased to 14

Name _____ Date _____

PRACTICE WORKSHEET 11-2

Frequency Tables

1. Complete the frequency column of this table.

Score	Tally	Frequency
1	7HL IIII	9
2	7HL 7HL IIII	14
3	7HL III	8
4	7HL 7HL 7HL 7HL II	22
5	7HL I	6
6	7HL 7HL 7HL III	18

Find each of the following.
Round to the nearest tenth.

2. mean **3.7**

3. median **4**

4. mode **4**

5. range **5**

Solve. Use the data at the right. Round to the nearest tenth.

6. Make a frequency table for this set of data.

Number of Children in each family

2	2	5	2	2
5	3	1	3	1
4	2	1	5	2
2	1	3	4	2

Number	Tally	Frequency
1	IIII	4
2	7HL III	8
3	III	3
4	II	2
5	III	3

7. Find the mean. **2.6**

8. Find the median. **2**

9. Find the mode. **2**

10. Find the range. **4**

11. Make a frequency table for this set of data.

Hours Practiced Each Week by Band Members

4	3	7	7	4
4	7	4	9	3
3	5	9	9	9
4	4	5	3	7
7	7	5	4	4

Number	Tally	Frequency
3	IIII	4
4	7HL III	8
5	III	3
7	7HL I	6
9	IIII	4

12. Find the mean. **5.5 h**

13. Find the median. **5 h**

14. Find the mode. **4 h**

15. Find the range. **6 h**

ANSWER KEY

PRACTICE WORKSHEET 11-3

Applications: Misusing Statistics

The commissions earned last month by salespeople at Electronics City are shown at the right.

Commission	Number of Salespeople
$ 500	7
$ 800	5
$1,000	3
$2,200	1
$2,800	2
$5,400	2

1. Find the mean, median, and mode of the commission amounts earned.
$1,455; $800; $500
2. Which "average" would you use in an advertisement to hire new salespeople? Why?
The mean; it is the highest.
3. Which "average" best describes the commission earned by all salespeople? Why?
The median; only $\frac{1}{4}$ of the salespeople earn more than the mean and more than $\frac{1}{2}$ earn more than the mode.

The number of yards a football player gained by rushing during each game of a season are shown at the right.

38	42	54	47
46	62	64	58

4. Find the mean and median of the yards rushed per game to the nearest tenth.
51.4; 50.5
5. Which "average" best describes the yards rushed per game? Why?
Accept either mean or median.
6. Instead of rushing for 38 yards in one game, suppose the player rushed for 102 yards. How would the mean and median be affected?
higher mean—59.4; higher median—56
7. Now which "average" best describes the yards rushed per game? Why?
The median; in only $\frac{1}{4}$ of the games did the player rush for more than the mean.

The prices of different camcorders carried by a store are listed at the right.

$ 899
$ 999
$ 950
$1,950
$1,099

8. Find the mean and median prices.
$1,179.40; $999
9. Which "average" best describes the price of a camcorder? Why?
The median; only one is priced higher than the mean.
10. Suppose that the store replaces the most expensive camcorder with a model priced at $1,100. How would the mean and median be affected?
lower mean—$1,009.40; median not affected

PRACTICE WORKSHEET 11-4

Bar Graphs

Make a vertical bar graph for each set of data.

1.
Average Points Scored per Basketball Game	
Wildcats	62
Rockets	74
Panthers	85
Bulldogs	78
Jets	87
Cougars	66

2.
1988 Population	
Chicago	3,000,000
Houston	1,700,000
Los Angeles	3,400,000
New York	7,400,000
Philadelphia	1,600,000

Make a horizontal bar graph for each set of data.

3.
Annual Rainfall (in inches)	
1987	45
1988	32
1989	27
1990	35
1991	48

4.
Average Miles per Gallon of Gas	
Car A	32
Car B	26
Car C	22
Car D	28
Car E	31
Car F	24

PRACTICE WORKSHEET 11-5

Line Graphs

Make a line graph for each set of data.

1.
Price per Gallon of Regular Gasoline	
1965	$0.31
1970	$0.36
1975	$0.58
1980	$1.19
1985	$1.12

2.
Minimum Hourly Wage Rate	
1950	$0.75
1960	$1.00
1970	$1.60
1980	$3.10
1990	$3.35

3.
Motor Vehicle Registrations	
1935	26.2 million
1945	31.0 million
1955	62.7 million
1965	90.4 million
1975	132.9 million
1985	171.7 million

4.
Average Speed of Indianapolis 500 Winners (in mph)	
1960	139
1965	151
1970	156
1975	159
1980	143
1985	153
1990	186

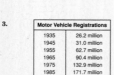

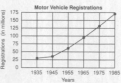

PRACTICE WORKSHEET 11-6

Pictographs

Make a pictograph for each set of data.

1.
TVs Sold	
January	20
February	18
March	5
April	24
May	12
June	9

2.
Pennant Sales	
Sunday	50
Monday	35
Tuesday	25
Wednesday	20
Thursday	40

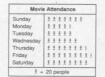

3.
Movie Attendance	
Sunday	140
Monday	90
Tuesday	100
Wednesday	120
Thursday	150
Friday	170
Saturday	160

4.
Music Store Sales	
Rock	8,500
Classical	4,250
Country	4,000
Other	3,750

ANSWER KEY

Name _____ Date _____

PRACTICE WORKSHEET 11-7

Circle Graphs

Make a circle graph for each set of data.

1.

Redalgo Family Budget	
Food	25%
Housing	30%
Clothing	15%
Transportation	15%
Recreation	10%
Other	5%

Redalgo Family Budget

2.

Materials Used to Generate Power in the U.S.	
Oil	50%
Gas	25%
Coal	15%
Nuclear	5%
Water	5%

Materials Used to Generate Power in the U.S.

3.

Attendance at Concert	
Children	10%
Teens	40%
Adults	35%
Senior Citizens	15%

Attendance at Concert

4.

Sales of Electronics	
TVs	30%
VCRs	20%
Stereo equipment	25%
Personal computers	10%
Video games	10%
Other	5%

Sales of Electronics

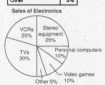

Glencoe Division, Macmillan/McGraw-Hill

121

Name _____ Date _____

PRACTICE WORKSHEET 11-8

Stem-and-Leaf Plots

State the stems that you would use to plot each set of data.

1. 72, 85, 53, 57, 74, 79   5, 7, 8   **2.** 26, 3, 38, 15, 29, 36   0, 1, 2, 3

3. 1.4, 2.8, 1.9, 3.7, 2.6, 4.5   1, 2, 3, 4   **4.** 536, 738, 104, 427, 326, 258   10, 25, 32, 42, 53, 73

Find the median and mode of the data in each stem-and-leaf plot.

5.

Stem	Leaf
4	1 2 5
5	3 5 7
6	4 5 6 8

56; none

6.

Stem	Leaf
2	3 5 9
3	4 6 8 9
4	2 3 3 7

38, 43

7.

Stem	Leaf
0	3 7 7 8
1	2 4 8 9
2	0 1 1 3
3	2 5 8

19; 7 and 21

Use the ages at the right to complete problems 8–11.

15	6	19	24	37	58	24
8	27	39	18	54	25	32
50	35	31	53	9	28	

8. Construct a stem-and-leaf plot of the data.

9. What is the youngest age?   6

10. What is the range of the ages?   52

11. How many ages are above 20?   14

Stem	Leaf
0	6 8 9
1	5 8 9
2	4 4 5 7 8
3	1 2 5 7 9
5	0 3 4 8

12. Use the data at the right to construct a stem-and-leaf plot. In which interval were the most jeans priced? $30–$39

Prices of Different Style Jeans (in dollars)					
24	19	36	29	37	32	27
25	60	32	62	45	29	37	42
19	44	36	28	40	37	31	58

Stem	Leaf
1	9 9
2	4 5 7 8 9 9
3	1 2 2 6 6 7 7 7
4	0 2 2 4 5
5	8
6	0 2

Glencoe Division, Macmillan/McGraw-Hill

122

Name _____ Date _____

PRACTICE WORKSHEET 11-9

Measures of Variation

Find the upper quartile, lower quartile, and interquartile range for each set of data.

1. 2, 5, 7, 9, 10, 12, 14, 18   13; 6; 7

2. 17, 18, 54, 57, 60, 62, 74, 76, 80, 81   76; 54; 22

3. 39, 48, 57, 24, 35, 32, 42, 56   52; 33.5; 18.5

4. 64, 27, 39, 56, 57, 16, 60, 72, 38, 41   60; 38; 22

5.

Stem	Leaf
2	4 5
3	0 1 2
4	5 8
5	2 4 9

6.

Stem	Leaf
0	4
1	1 1 5 6 8
2	3 4
3	2 7

7.

Stem	Leaf
5	0 0 1 3
6	5 8 8
7	1 2 4
8	7 9

8.

Stem	Leaf
8	2 4
9	3 5 6 8 9
10	2 4 7 8
11	2

2 | 4 represents 24.   3 | 2 represents 32.   5 | 0 represents 50.   11 | 2 represents 112.

52; 30; 22   24; 11; 13   73; 52; 21   105.5; 94; 11.5

Solve. Use the data at the right.

9. Make a stem-and-leaf plot for each store's data.

Rags & Riches

Stem	Leaf
1	4 6
2	2 4 5
3	6 8
4	2 8 9
5	2 4

Jean Joint

Stem	Leaf
1	5
2	4 8 9
3	2 2 5 7 8 9
4	0
5	7

10. Find the interquartile range of each store's data.
Rags & Riches—25.5; Jean Joint—10

11. From your findings in Problem 10, which store has the more consistent number of customers per hour?
Jean Joint

Customers per Hour		
Time	Rags & Riches	Jean Joint
10:00-10:59	24	15
11:00-11:59	36	32
12:00-12:59	54	57
1:00- 1:59	42	38
2:00- 2:59	38	29
3:00- 3:59	14	28
4:00- 4:59	52	35
5:00- 5:59	49	39
6:00- 6:59	22	40
7:00- 7:59	48	32
8:00- 8:59	25	37
9:00- 9:59	16	24

Glencoe Division, Macmillan/McGraw-Hill

123

Name _____ Date _____

PRACTICE WORKSHEET 11-10

Box-and-Whisker Plots

The number of hours worked in one month by part-time salespeople at Discount Mart is displayed at the right. Use this box-and-whisker plot to answer each question.

1. Which of these pieces of information can be found on this box-and-whisker plot: mean, median, mode, range?
median and range

2. What is the range of the data?
50

3. What part of the data is greater than 50?
one-fourth

4. The middle half of the data is between what two numbers?
30 and 50

5. State the median, upper and lower quartiles, and the interquartile range of the data.
45; 50; 30; 20

The fuel efficiency of twelve different cars was tested, and the data are shown at the right. Use these data for Problems 6–9.

Miles per Gallon of Gas				
19	21	20	38	42	28
24	37	33	18	26	20

6. Construct a box-and-whisker plot of the data.

7. Find the mean, median, mode, and range of the data. Which of these pieces of information could you find from the box-and-whisker plot?
$27\frac{1}{6}$; 25; 20; 24; median and range

8. What part of the data is greater than 25?
one-half

9. State the upper and lower quartiles and the interquartile range of the data.
35; 20; 15

Glencoe Division, Macmillan/McGraw-Hill

124

PRACTICE WORKSHEET 11-11

Problem-Solving Strategy: Look for a Pattern
Solve.

1. Rhonda swam 4 laps the first day, 6 laps the second day, 8 laps the third day, and so on until she could swim 20 laps. How many days did it take her to reach 20 laps?
9 days

2. A dropped ball from a high place falls 32 ft the first second, 32 ft × 4 the second second, and 32 ft × 9 the third second. How far does it fall the fifth second?
32 ft × 25, or 800 ft

3. From one corner of a four-sided figure, one diagonal can be drawn. From one corner of a five-sided figure, two diagonals can be drawn. How many diagonals can be drawn from one corner of a nine-sided figure?

6 diagonals

4. Tina started working at an hourly wage of $4.40. She will get a 20¢ raise every 6 months. What will be her hourly rate after working 3 years?
$5.60

5. Each of the 8 people at the party exchanges greetings with each other person at the party. How many exchanges of greeting are there?
28 exchanges

6. A new music store had 20 customers the first day it was open. The number of customers doubled each day for the next four days. How many customers did the store have on the fifth day?
320 customers

7. Sixteen teams are involved in a single-elimination tournament. When a team loses, it is eliminated. How many games are needed to determine this tournament's winner?
15 games

8. Danny plans to do 5 more push-ups each day until he can do 75. He begins with 15. How many days will it take him?
13 days

PRACTICE WORKSHEET 12-1

Integers
Replace ○ with <, >, or = to make a true sentence.

1. $-12 \bigcirc 15$ **<**
2. $6 \bigcirc 18$ **<**
3. $13 \bigcirc -21$ **>**
4. $9 \bigcirc 6$ **>**
5. $-2.3 \bigcirc -2.2$ **<**
6. $-4 \bigcirc -12$ **>**
7. $-7 \bigcirc 7$ **<**
8. $-7 \bigcirc 5$ **<**
9. $0 \bigcirc -2$ **>**
10. $|18| \bigcirc |-14|$ **>**
11. $|-13| \bigcirc |-15|$ **<**
12. $|-12| \bigcirc |12|$ **=**
13. $|-3| \bigcirc |7|$ **<**
14. $|0| \bigcirc |-5|$ **<**
15. $|-10| \bigcirc |4|$ **>**
16. $|8| \bigcirc |-8|$ **=**
17. $|-13| \bigcirc |-6|$ **>**
18. $|4| \bigcirc |-11|$ **<**

Order from least to greatest.

19. 5, 8, -2, 0, -4
-4, -2, 0, 5, 8
20. -1, 6, 2, 5, -3
-3, -1, 2, 5, 6
21. 1, 0, -1, -8, -7, -3
-8, -7, -3, -1, 0, 1
22. 1, -6, 4, -4, 7, -1
-6, -4, -1, 1, 4, 7
23. 0, -7, 2, -9, 5, 3
-9, -7, 0, 2, 3, 5
24. 1, 4, -2, 8, -5, -9
-9, -5, -2, 1, 4, 8
25. 4, -3, 7, 1, 0, -2
-3, -2, 0, 1, 4, 7
26. 5, -2, -5, 0, 2, 1
-5, -2, 0, 1, 2, 5
27. -7, 2, -1, -9, 3
-9, -7, -1, 2, 3
28. 1, -3, -5, 4, -2, 6
-5, -3, -2, 1, 4, 6

Complete.

29. If -6 indicates a drop of 6°C in temperature, what does 6 indicate?
a rise of 6°C

30. If 31 indicates 31 seconds after a rocket launch, what does -31 indicate?
31 s before launch

PRACTICE WORKSHEET 12-2

Adding Integers
Write an equation for each number line. Then solve.

1.
$-5 + 3 = n; -2$

2.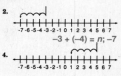
$-3 + (-4) = n; -7$

3.
$-6 + 6 = n; 0$

4.
$5 + (-4) = n; 1$

Add. Use a number line if necessary.

5. $21 + (-8)$ **13**
6. $-6 + 4$ **-2**
7. $13 + (-19)$ **-6**
8. $-2 + 6$ **4**
9. $41 + 3$ **44**
10. $-7 + (-5)$ **-12**
11. $-12 + (-15)$ **-27**
12. $3 + (-3)$ **0**
13. $-1.1 + (-2)$ **-3.1**
14. $4.3 + 1.3$ **5.6**
15. $-5.2 + 3.4$ **-1.8**
16. $9 + (-7)$ **2**
17. $-7 + 11$ **4**
18. $-4.2 + (-8.5)$ **-12.7**
19. $3 + 5$ **8**
20. $-3 + 15$ **12**
21. $\frac{4}{5} + \left(-\frac{3}{10}\right)$ **$\frac{1}{2}$**
22. $1 + (-7)$ **-6**
23. $-\frac{1}{2} + \left(-\frac{3}{4}\right)$ **$-1\frac{1}{4}$**
24. $-\frac{2}{3} + \frac{5}{12}$ **$-\frac{1}{4}$**
25. $6 + (-8)$ **-2**

Solve.

26. The balance in Sally's checking account was $273.25. She wrote a check for $72.15 and made a deposit of $55.20. What is her new balance?
$256.30

27. The plane was flying at 7,800 feet when it had to climb 2,500 feet to clear a mountain range. What was its new altitude?
10,300 ft

28. Mark had business on the twenty-seventh floor. Later he went up 6 floors to the rooftop observatory. On what floor is the observatory?
thirty-third floor

29. Starting on their own 25-yard line, the Packers gain 8 yards, lose 5 yards, and gain 7 yards. What yard line are they on now?
35-yard line

PRACTICE WORKSHEET 12-3

Subtracting Integers
Subtract.

1. $9 - (-2)$ **11**
2. $-12 - (-5)$ **-7**
3. $-3 - 16$ **-19**
4. $2 - (-8)$ **10**
5. $15 - 6$ **9**
6. $-14 - 3$ **-17**
7. $-11 - (-7)$ **-4**
8. $1 - 13$ **-12**
9. $9 - 2$ **7**
10. $-25 - (-16)$ **-9**
11. $32 - (-7)$ **39**
12. $-3 - 21$ **-24**
13. $72 - (-8)$ **80**
14. $61 - (-55)$ **116**
15. $1.9 - (-2.1)$ **4**
16. $-3 - (-5)$ **2**
17. $-1 - 4$ **-5**
18. $-1.6 - 1.6$ **-3.2**
19. $2 - 8$ **-6**
20. $0.3 - (-1.9)$ **2.2**
21. $4 - (-1)$ **5**
22. $5 - (-5)$ **10**
23. $\frac{1}{6} - \frac{3}{4}$ **$-\frac{7}{12}$**
24. $-\frac{5}{6} - \frac{1}{3}$ **$-1\frac{1}{6}$**
25. $\frac{7}{8} - \left(-\frac{1}{4}\right)$ **$1\frac{1}{8}$**
26. $-10 - 5$ **-15**

Solve.

27. Rocky's Flower Shop deposited checks and cash in the amount of $2,452.60 on Friday. On Monday the bank called to say that one of the checks had been returned. If that check was for $45.87, what was the actual deposit on Friday?
$2,406.73

28. When Lucy received her checking account statement, it showed a balance of $515.63. Lucy's check register showed a deposit of $253.62 and two checks for $21.75 and $37.89 which were not included in the statement. What is Lucy's actual account balance?
$709.61

29. Bob wrote a check for $15.75 to pay for a ticket to the symphony. The check was returned because the tickets had all been sold. Bob's check register showed a balance of $372.15. What is his new balance?
$387.90

30. Jenny's balance was $349.95. She deposited three checks, $45.00, $125.63, and $38.25. She also withdrew $50.00 in cash. What is her new balance after these transactions?
$508.83

ANSWER KEY

Name _____ Date _____

PRACTICE WORKSHEET 12-4

Applications: Windchill Factor

Windchill Chart

Wind speed in mph	Actual temperature (°Fahrenheit)								
	50	40	30	20	10	0	-10	-20	-30
	Equivalent temperature (°Fahrenheit)								
0	50	40	30	20	10	0	-10	-20	-30
5	48	37	27	16	6	-5	-15	-26	-36
10	40	28	16	4	-9	-21	-33	-46	-58
15	36	22	9	-5	-18	-36	-45	-58	-72
20	32	18	4	-10	-25	-39	-53	-67	-82
25	30	16	0	-15	-29	-44	-59	-74	-88
30	28	13	-2	-18	-33	-48	-63	-79	-94

Use the chart above to find each equivalent temperature.

1. 40°F, 5 mph
   37°F
2. −10°F, 20 mph
   −53°F
3. 0°F, 15 mph
   −36°F
4. 50°F, 10 mph
   40°F
5. −20°F, 30 mph
   −79°F
6. 20°F, 10 mph
   4°F
7. 40°F, 25 mph
   16°F
8. 30°F, 0 mph
   30°F
9. 10°F, 5 mph
   6°F
10. −20°F, 15 mph
   −58°F
11. −30°F, 30 mph
   −48°F
12. −30°F, 0 mph
   −30°F

What is the difference between each actual temperature and the equivalent temperature when the wind speed is 10 mph?

13. 40°F
   12°F
14. −20°F
   26°F
15. 0°F
   21°F
16. −30°F
   28°F
17. 10°F
   19°F
18. 20°F
   16°F

Solve.

19. The actual temperature is −20°F. The equivalent temperature with the windchill factor is −74°F. What is the wind speed?
   25 mph

20. The wind speed is 15 mph. The equivalent temperature with the windchill factor is 9°F. What is the actual temperature?
   30°F

Name _____ Date _____

PRACTICE WORKSHEET 12-5

Multiplying Integers

Multiply.

1. $9 \times (-2)$ **−18**
2. $-12 \times (-5)$ **60**
3. -3×16 **−48**
4. $2 \times (-8)$ **−16**
5. 15×6 **90**
6. -14×3 **−42**
7. $-11 \times (-7)$ **77**
8. 1×13 **13**
9. 9×15 **135**
10. $-25 \times (-16)$ **400**
11. $30 \times (-7)$ **−210**
12. -3×21 **−63**
13. $70 \times (-80)$ **−5,600**
14. $61 \times (-59)$ **−3,599**
15. $9.1 \times (-1.9)$ **−17.29**
16. $-3.8 \times (-5.2)$ **19.76**
17. -6×0 **0**
18. -1.5×1.5 **−2.25**
19. -7×8 **−56**
20. $7 \times (-21)$ **−147**
21. $0 \times (-2)$ **0**
22. $-\frac{2}{3} \times \left(-\frac{3}{4}\right)$ **$\frac{1}{2}$**
23. $-\frac{3}{4} \times \frac{1}{6}$ **$-\frac{1}{8}$**
24. $6 \times (-10)$ **−60**
25. $\frac{8}{9} \times \left(-\frac{1}{4}\right)$ **$-\frac{2}{9}$**
26. $-4 \times (-25)$ **100**

Solve.

27. A deep-sea exploring ship is pulling up a diver at the rate of 25 feet per minute. The diver is 200 feet below sea level. How deep was the diver 10 minutes ago?
   450 feet below sea level

28. Joe is playing a game with a regular die. If the number that turns up is even, he will gain 5 times the number that comes up. If it is odd, he will lose 10 times the number that comes up. He tosses a 3. Express the result as an integer.
   −30

29. Barb's Swimsuit Outlet sold 312 swimsuits during a special sale where every suit was marked down to $9.99. Twenty-nine suits were returned for refunds. What was the actual income from the sale?
   $2,827.17

30. After a concert was canceled, ticket holders could exchange tickets for a future date or get a refund of the $20 price. Seven hundred tickets were returned for refunds. Express this income as an integer.
   −14,000

Name _____ Date _____

PRACTICE WORKSHEET 12-6

Dividing Integers

Divide.

1. $18 \div (-3)$ **−6**
2. $-48 \div (-12)$ **4**
3. $-45 \div 15$ **−3**
4. $40 \div (-8)$ **−5**
5. $0 \div 0$ **0**
6. $-63 \div 3$ **−21**
7. $-140 \div (-7)$ **20**
8. $52 \div 13$ **4**
9. $-40 \div (-5)$ **8**
10. $-120 \div (-6)$ **20**
11. $168 \div (-7)$ **−24**
12. $-210 \div 21$ **−10**
13. $5,680 \div (-80)$ **−71**
14. $27 \div (-9)$ **−3**
15. $0 \div (-1)$ **0**
16. $-7.2 \div (-0.9)$ **8**
17. $-14.64 \div 4$ **−3.66**
18. $-15 \div 1.5$ **−10**
19. $14 \div (-10)$ **−1.4**
20. $-25 \div (5)$ **−5**
21. $4.4 \div (-2.2)$ **−2**
22. $-\frac{2}{3} \div \left(-\frac{4}{9}\right)$ **$1\frac{1}{2}$**
23. $-\frac{3}{4} \div \frac{1}{8}$ **−6**
24. $-80 \div (-4)$ **20**
25. $\frac{8}{9} \div \left(-\frac{4}{15}\right)$ **$-3\frac{1}{3}$**
26. $-4 \div 8$ **−0.5**
27. $-18 \div 6$ **−3**
28. $51 \div (-3)$ **−17**
29. $-91 \div (-13)$ **7**
30. $-42 \div 14$ **−3**
31. $-96 \div (-24)$ **4**
32. $90 \div (-15)$ **−6**

Solve.

33. Stan weighed 225 pounds on March 1. Four months later he weighed 197 pounds. What was his average change in weight per month?
   loss of 7 lb or −7 lb

34. In 1980, the population of Clayborn was 15,792. In 1986 the population was 19,296. What was the average change in population per year?
   increase of 584 or 584

Name _____ Date _____

PRACTICE WORKSHEET 12-7

Problem-Solving Strategy: Work Backwards

Solve. Work backwards.

1. Eight times a number plus 7 is equal to 79. Find the number.
   9

2. Twice a number decreased by 12 is equal to 10. Find the number.
   11

3. Seven more than 3 times a number is equal to 49. Find the number.
   14

4. If 8 is added to a number and then the number is divided by 3, the result is 12. Find the number.
   28

5. Nine less than 6 times a number is equal to 93. Find the number.
   17

6. If the sum of a number and 10 is divided by 3, the result is 13. Find the number.
   29

7. If a number is multiplied by 4, then 6 is added to it, and the result is divided by 7, the answer is 6. Find the number.
   9

8. If a number is divided by 8 and then 12 is added to the quotient, the result is 17. Find the number.
   40

ANSWER KEY

PRACTICE WORKSHEET 13-1

Solving Equations Using Addition or Subtraction
Solve each equation. Check your solution.

1. $13 = 9 + a$ **2.** $15 + b = -38$ **3.** $72 = a - 7$ **4.** $b - 15 = -38$
4   −53   79   −23

5. $t + (-27) = -10$ **6.** $4 + c = 9$ **7.** $c - (-8) = -17$ **8.** $-26 + r = 215$
17   5   −25   241

9. $d - 4 = 9$ **10.** $e - 117 = -215$ **11.** $28 + x = 9$ **12.** $f - 57 = -121$
13   −98   −19   −64

13. $8 = s + 1\frac{3}{5}$ **14.** $k + (-0.7) = -1.1$ **15.** $4 = g - 3\frac{3}{5}$ **16.** $h - 35 = 27$
$6\frac{2}{5}$ −0.4 $7\frac{3}{5}$ 62

17. $-13.2 + y = 10$ **18.** $n - 2.7 = 2.7$ **19.** $p - (-0.3) = -0.8$ **20.** $g + 0.3 = 0.8$
23.2   5.4   −1.1   0.5

21. $q - 6.6 = -1.4$ **22.** $t + 86 = -14$ **23.** $v + (-1.7) = 3.2$ **24.** $r - 7.1 = 3.2$
5.2   −100   4.9   10.3

Solve.

25. The high temperature today after a morning low of −10°F, is 25°F. How many degrees did the temperature rise?
35°F

26. There were 27 students in the library. Four left and then another group came in, bringing the total to 45. How many were in that group?
22 students

27. Bob is on a weight-loss program. He has lost 15.2 pounds so far. If he now weighs 197 pounds, how much did he weigh when he began?
212.2 lb

28. Jane has $382.57 in her checking account. After writing a check for $451.25, what is her balance?
−$68.68

PRACTICE WORKSHEET 13-2

Solving Equations Using Multiplication or Division
Solve each equation. Check your solution.

1. $9 = \frac{a}{3}$ **2.** $84 = 7a$ **3.** $15b = -60$ **4.** $25 = \frac{b}{10}$
27   12   −4   250

5. $c + (-5) = 9$ **6.** $-4d = 0$ **7.** $\frac{d}{6} = -15$ **8.** $-4 = \frac{e}{-12}$
−45   0   −90   48

9. $-11e = -77$ **10.** $10 = g + 7$ **11.** $6 = \frac{3}{4}g$ **12.** $-\frac{2}{3}j = 22$
7   70   8   −33

13. $h + 8 = 25$ **14.** $39 = -13k$ **15.** $75 = 25l$ **16.** $-7 = \frac{j}{2}$
200   −3   3   −14

17. $-56 = \frac{k}{-10}$ **18.** $-24 = 2m$ **19.** $\frac{m}{-5} = 2.25$ **20.** $27n = 27$
560   −12   −11.25   1

21. $3p = -45$ **22.** $12 = \frac{p}{-6}$ **23.** $11 = \frac{q}{9}$ **24.** $-6q = 3.6$
−15   −72   99   −0.6

Solve.

25. The product of two numbers is 12. Their sum is −7. What are the numbers?
−3 and −4

26. The quotient of two numbers is −1. Their difference is 8. What are the numbers?
−4 and 4

27. When the cold front moved through, the temperature fell 24°F in 4 hours. What was the average temperature rise or fall per hour?
fall of 6°F

28. Brandon, Maria, Tonya, and Conrad shared the cost of a $12.76 pizza equally. What was each person's share?
$3.19

PRACTICE WORKSHEET 13-3

Solving Two-Step Equations
Solve each equation. Check your solution.

1. $\frac{d}{6} + 7 = 18$ **2.** $2a + 7 = -3$ **3.** $3(p - 5) = 75$ **4.** $5t + (-32) = 43$
66   −5   30   15

5. $2 + 5c = 17$ **6.** $\frac{j}{3} + 4 = -2$ **7.** $\frac{b}{-5} - 9 = 16$ **8.** $-2(2 + y) = 6$
3   −18   −125   −5

9. $-42 = \frac{a}{3} - 9$ **10.** $25 = -3b - 2$ **11.** $\frac{c - 20}{-5} = -2$ **12.** $-18 = 5g + (-3)$
−99   −9   30   −3

13. $-81 = 5e - 6$ **14.** $5 = \frac{f}{-4} - 3$ **15.** $3(d - 3) = -15$ **16.** $42 = -5k + 2$
−15   −32   −2   −8

17. $-11 = \frac{j}{3} - 2$ **18.** $\frac{2}{3}(h + 5) = 4$ **19.** $25 = \frac{l}{3} + 26$ **20.** $-2 + 6m = 22$
−27   9   −3   4

Solve.

21. Four times a number is added to 12. The result is −28. What is the number?
−10

22. Half of a number is subtracted from 19. The result is 13. What is the number?
12

23. If Marilyn buys 3 more compact discs, she will have twice as many discs as Sharon. Sharon has 12 discs. How many discs does Marilyn have?
21 discs

24. Milton is $30 short of having half the money he needs to buy a $400 bicycle. How much money does Milton have?
$170

PRACTICE WORKSHEET 13-4

The Coordinate Plane
Find the ordered pair for each point labeled on the coordinate plane.

1. A   (2, 3) **2.** B   (−2, 5)
3. C   (4, −4) **4.** D   (0, −3)
5. E   (−5, 5) **6.** F   (6, −1)
7. G   (−1, 0) **8.** H   (−5, −6)

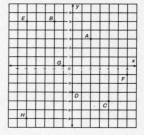

Draw coordinate axes on the grid at the right. Graph each ordered pair. Label each point with the given letter.

9. A (3, 4) **10.** B (−2, 1)
11. C (−5, −5) **12.** D (2, −1)
13. E (2, 3) **14.** F (−2, 5)
15. G (−1, 0) **16.** H (0, −1)
17. J (−2, −3) **18.** K (2, 5)
19. L (−5, 2) **20.** M (5, 5)
21. N (1, 2) **22.** P (−1, −1)
23. Q (4, 5) **24.** R (5, −4)

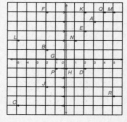

ANSWER KEY

Name _____ Date _____

PRACTICE WORKSHEET 13-5

Graphing Equations

Graph the solutions to each equation.

1. $3x = y$

2. $-4x = y$

3. $y = x + 3$

4. $x - 2 = y$

5. $\frac{2}{5}x = y$

6. $x + y = 1$

7. $x - y = 3$

8. $y = \frac{x}{4}$

9. $x + y = 0$

Name _____ Date _____

PRACTICE WORKSHEET 13-6

Applications: Reading a Grid Map

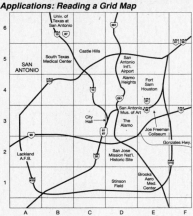

Use the map above.

1. What hospital is located in B-5?
South Texas Medical Center

2. What airport is located in D-1?
Stinson Field

3. What highway is the University of Texas at San Antonio near? **10/87**

4. What highway passes through Lackland Air Force Base? **410**

5. Which highways would you travel to go from City Hall to San Antonio International Airport? **81/87 and 281**

Give the location of each as a letter-number pair.

6. Joe Freeman Coliseum **E-3**

7. Castle Hills **C-5**

8. San Antonio Museum of Art **D-3**

9. Alamo Heights **D-4**

10. San Jose Mission National Historic Site **D-2**

11. Gonzales Highway **E-2, F-2**

Name _____ Date _____

PRACTICE WORKSHEET 13-7

Problem-Solving Strategy: Writing an Equation

Solve. Write an equation.

1. Sheila has 5 fewer tapes than Cheryl. Together they have 33 tapes. How many tapes does each girl have?

$(x - 5) + x = 33$; Sheila—14 tapes; Cheryl—19 tapes

2. Ted's highest bowling scores is 236. This is 10 less than three times his lowest score. What is Ted's lowest score?

$236 = 3x - 10$; 82

3. Movie attendance at the 7:00 show was 342. This is 25 more than half the number of people who attended the 9:00 show. How many attended the 9:00 show?

$342 = \frac{1}{2}x + 25$; 634 people

4. Jody jogged and cycled a total of 130 miles last week. The number of miles she jogged is 2 more than one-third the number of miles she cycled. How many miles did she jog? Cycle?

$130 = x + \frac{1}{3}x + 2$; jog—34 mi; cycle—96 mi

5. A bookstore displayed 110 copies of the #1 bestseller in 12 rows. Five rows contained 2 fewer books than the other rows. How many books were in each row?

$110 = 7x + 5(x - 2)$; 5 rows had 8 books; 7 rows had 10 books

6. Marla earned $39 baby-sitting this week. On Saturday she baby-sat 1 hour more than twice the number of hours she baby-sat on Friday. If she earns $3 per hour, how many hours did she baby-sit each day?

$39 = 3(x + 2x + 1)$; Friday—4 h; Saturday—9 h

Name _____ Date _____

PRACTICE WORKSHEET 14-1

Finding the Number of Outcomes

Use multiplication to find the number of possible outcomes. Draw a tree diagram to show the possible outcomes.

1. tossing a nickel, a dime, and a quarter **8**

nickel   dime   quarter   outcomes

2. a choice of blue or white jeans with a red, black, or green sweater **6**

jeans   sweater   outcomes

3. a choice of a small, medium, or large pizza with thin or thick crust and pepperoni, sausage, or Canadian bacon **18**

size   crust   topping   outcomes

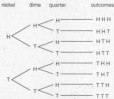

4. choosing a sedan, hatchback, station wagon, or convertible in white, gray, or red with a manual or automatic transmission **24**

style   color   transmission   outcomes

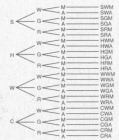

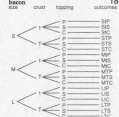

ANSWER KEY

PRACTICE WORKSHEET 14-2

Probability and Percents

There are two red marbles, one green marble, and one yellow marble in a bag. One marble is chosen. Find the probability that each event will occur.

1. a red marble
50%

2. a yellow marble
25%

3. a red or a green marble
75%

4. a yellow or a green marble
50%

5. *not* a green marble
75%

6. a blue marble
0%

There are two black, four red, three purple, and one orange marker in a box. One marker is chosen. Find the probability the event will occur.

7. a red marker
40%

8. a black or a purple marker
50%

9. *not* an orange marker
90%

10. a green marker
0%

11. a red, a purple, or an orange marker
80%

12. *not* a red or a purple marker
30%

Each spinner at the right is spun once. Find the probability of spinning each of the following. Round to the nearest whole percent. (Hint: First make a list of the possible combinations of spins.)

13. a 3 on both spinners
6%

14. a 2 on the first spinner and a 4 on the second spinner
6%

15. a 1 on one spinner and a 3 on the other
13%

16. both numbers the same
25%

17. both numbers less than 4
56%

18. a 3 on exactly one spinner
38%

19. a 3 on at least one spinner
44%

20. one number less than the other
75%

PRACTICE WORKSHEET 14-3

Multiplying Probabilities

A bag contains four red, five white, and three blue marbles. Suppose you choose a marble from the bag and then choose another marble without replacing the first one. Find the probability of choosing each event.

1. white both times
$\frac{5}{33}$

2. blue both times
$\frac{1}{22}$

3. red both times
$\frac{1}{11}$

4. same color both times
$\frac{19}{66}$

5. red, then white
$\frac{5}{33}$

6. white, then red
$\frac{5}{33}$

7. white, then blue
$\frac{5}{44}$

8. red, then green
0

Suppose you choose a marble from the bag described above, replace it, and then choose another. Find the probability of choosing each event.

9. white both times
$\frac{25}{144}$

10. blue both times
$\frac{1}{16}$

11. red both times
$\frac{1}{9}$

12. same color both times
$\frac{25}{72}$

13. red, then white
$\frac{5}{36}$

14. white, then red
$\frac{5}{36}$

15. white, then blue
$\frac{5}{48}$

16. red, then green
0

Solve.

17. A card is drawn from the deck shown below. Then another card is drawn without replacing the first. What is the probability that the cards drawn will be 2, 3 or 3, 2?
$\frac{4}{15}$

18. A card is selected at random from the group shown below. A second card is drawn without replacing the first. What is the probability that both cards will have odd numbers on them?
$\frac{2}{5}$

PRACTICE WORKSHEET 14-4

Adding Probabilities

Find each probability. Use the spinner at the right.

1. P(w or t)
$\frac{1}{4}$

2. P(a consonant or a vowel)
1

3. P(a vowel or striped)
$\frac{3}{4}$

4. P(a consonant or white)
$\frac{7}{8}$

Find each probability. Use the cards below.

5. P(an odd number or 2)
$\frac{2}{3}$

6. P(3 or 8)
$\frac{1}{3}$

7. P(an even number or white)
$\frac{3}{4}$

8. P(gray or a prime number)
$\frac{3}{4}$

9. P(an odd number or 1)
$\frac{5}{12}$

10. P(an even number or a prime number)
$\frac{5}{6}$

The different color shapes below are placed in a box. One shape is drawn from the box. Find each probability.

11. P(a triangle or a quadrilateral)
$\frac{7}{9}$

12. P(a red shape or a circle)
$\frac{5}{9}$

13. P(a triangle that is blue)
$\frac{1}{9}$

14. P(a blue shape or a square)
$\frac{5}{9}$

15. P(a red shape or a polygon)
$\frac{7}{9}$

16. P(a yellow shape or a triangle)
$\frac{4}{9}$

PRACTICE WORKSHEET 14-5

Applications: Marketing Research

A company surveyed 120 people about their favorite radio station and the amount of time they listen to the radio each day. The results are shown in the tables below.

Favorite Radio Station	Number of People
KALM	28
KOOL	32
KLAS	15
KRZY	34
none	11

Time Spent Listening to Radio Daily	Number of People
more than 2 h	28
61 min–2 h	30
1 min–1 h	50
0 min	12

Find the probability of a person liking each station best.

1. KOOL
$\frac{4}{15}$

2. KOOL or KRZY
$\frac{11}{20}$

3. not KALM
$\frac{23}{30}$

4. neither KALM nor KOOL
$\frac{1}{2}$

Find the probability of a person most likely listening to the radio for each time.

5. 1 min–1 h
$\frac{5}{12}$

6. more than 1 h
$\frac{29}{60}$

7. 2 h or less
$\frac{23}{30}$

8. not at all
$\frac{1}{10}$

Assuming that the choice of station and the amount of time spent listening are independent, find the probability of each combination of favorite station and time spent listening to the radio each day.

9. KRZY and more than 2 h
$\frac{119}{1,800}$

10. KALM and 61 min–2 h
$\frac{7}{120}$

11. not KOOL and 1 min–1 h
$\frac{11}{36}$

12. no favorite station and not listening at all
$\frac{11}{1,200}$

ANSWER KEY

Name _____ Date _____

PRACTICE WORKSHEET 14-6

Odds

A die is rolled. Find the odds for each roll.

1. a 6
   1 to 5
2. not an odd number
   3 to 3
3. a number less than 4
   3 to 3
4. a 5 or a 6
   2 to 4
5. a 9
   0 to 6
6. a 6 or a 1
   2 to 4
7. a 4, 3, or 1
   3 to 3
8. not a 2
   5 to 1
9. a 2 or an odd number
   4 to 2
10. a 3 or an 8
    1 to 5

Two dice are rolled. Find the odds for each roll.

11. both dice different
    30 to 6
12. a 3 and a 5
    2 to 34
13. a sum of 12
    1 to 35
14. a sum of 7
    6 to 30
15. a sum of 5 or 10
    7 to 29
16. a sum less than 5
    6 to 30
17. a sum of 1
    0 to 36
18. *not* a sum of 8
    31 to 5
19. a sum of 4 and a 2 on at least one die
    1 to 35
20. a sum of 5 and a 3 on one die
    2 to 34

Solve.

21. On a TV game show, the contestant is supposed to match the correct price with a prize. If four prices are shown, what are the odds of selecting the correct one at random?
    1 to 3
22. If two coins are tossed, what are the odd for both coins landing with the same side up? What are the odds for both coins landing heads?
    2 to 2; 1 to 3

Name _____ Date _____

PRACTICE WORKSHEET 14-7

Problem-Solving Strategy: Using Samples to Predict

Solve. Use the results of the survey below for Exercises 1–9. The sample is taken from 1,500 students.

What do you collect?	
Stamps	35
Coins	20
Baseball cards	80
Rocks	15

1. How many students are in the sample?
   150 students
2. What is the probability that a student collects baseball cards?
   $\frac{8}{15}$
3. Predict how many of the 1,500 students collect baseball cards.
   800 students
4. What is the probability that a student collects rocks?
   $\frac{1}{10}$
5. Predict how many of the 1,500 students collect rocks.
   150 students
6. What is the probability that a student collects coins?
   $\frac{2}{15}$
7. Predict how many of the 1,500 students collect coins.
   200 students
8. If there are 30 students in one class, predict how many collect coins.
   4 students
9. Is it possible that a student will not collect stamps, coins, baseball cards, or rocks?
   yes

Solve.

10. In a survey of 200 people in Westville, 150 plan to vote in the town election. What is the probability that a person in Westville will vote?
    $\frac{3}{4}$
11. Refer to Exercise 10. If the population of Westville is 14,000, predict how many people will vote.
    10,500 people
12. If the television ad that states five out of six people will buy a new toothpaste is correct, what is the probability that your neighbor will buy it?
    $\frac{5}{6}$
13. Refer to Exercise 12. If 3,000 supermarket customers are planning to buy toothpaste, predict how many will buy the new toothpaste.
    2,500 customers